FROM EAST HERTFORDSHIRE

Edited by Emma Marsden

First published in Great Britain in 2000 by
YOUNG WRITERS
Remus House,
Coltsfoot Drive,
Woodston,
Peterborough, PE2 9JX
Telephone (01733) 890066

HB ISBN 0 75431 840 0
SB ISBN 0 75431 841 9

FOREWORD

This year, the Young Writers' Future Voices competition proudly presents a showcase of the best poetic talent from over 42,000 up-and-coming writers nationwide.

Successful in continuing our aim of promoting writing and creativity in children, our regional anthologies give a vivid insight into the thoughts, emotions and experiences of today's younger generation, displaying their inventive writing in its originality.

The thought, effort, imagination and hard work put into each poem impressed us all and again the task of editing proved challenging due to the quality of entries received, but was nevertheless enjoyable. We hope you are as pleased as we are with the final selection and that you continue to enjoy *Future Voices From East Hertfordshire* for many years to come.

CONTENTS

Lauren Cooper	59
Ricky Ellis	60
Claire Taplin	61
Daniel Smith	62
Andrew Tweddell	62
Nicola Richardson	63
Katherine Harknett	64
Lynette Dinmore	64
Jacob Hoy	65
Frances Williams	65
Kylie Savage	66
Daniel Lawrence	66
Laura Cockerell	67
Charlotte Bowey	68
Stephanie Phillips	68
Michelle Hackney	69
Sophie Gosden	70
Natalie Taylor	71
Michaela Baronowski	72
Mark Hayden Smith	72
David Collins	73
Mark Cornish	73
Paul Isham	74
Kirsty Marsh	74
Paul Luckett	75
Jamie Aitchison	75
Leighanne Piggott	76
Lewis Richardson	76
Siobhan Tomsett	77
Stacey Crouch	78
Sean Burgess	78
Rikki Woolford	79
Lucy Evans	80
Jamie Vella	80
Hannah Davis	81
Liam Finnigan	81
Steven Banting	82
Louise McIntyre	82

Andrew Kent	83
James Forte	83
Peter Enefer	84
Steven Smith	84
Christopher Reddy	85
Nadia White	85
Matthew Ward	86

Presdales School

Hannah Softley	86
Charlotte Keens	87
Rebecca Selcuk	87
Laura Williams	88
Rebekah Harvey	88
Francesca Foy	89
Clare Levitt	89
Samantha Whitworth	90
Zoe Cookson	90
Sarah Bunyan	91
Natalie Newman	91
Georgina Duggan	92
Harriet Ainsworth-Smith	92
Melissa Tucker	93
Gemma L Hardy	93
Emma Reed	94
Charlotte McCarthy	94
Caroline Gooch	95
Becky Jarvest	96
Jennifer Gilbert	96
Stephanie Collier	97
Rosie Aldridge	97
Louise Blanchard	98
Olivia Coleman	98
Emma Reemer	99
Lucy Hughes	99
Anna Hunt	100
Claire Barker	100
Hannah Gibbs	101

Richard Hale School

The Poems

THE BALLAD OF A WORKING HORSE

One of a kind am I now,
Just call me the local bus,
Pulling through the squares of beautiful Brugge,
Always in a rush, rush, rush.

Straps digging into my skin,
But mustn't stop to grumble,
For short tempered drivers and long arms with whips,
Make me very hard working and humble.

Halfway stops for food and water,
A roof over my heavy tired head,
One precious day off every week,
Cobbles to lay on for a bed.

One day it all goes wrong,
On turning a corner without thought,
Into the front of the shop I crash,
I leave my mark, a lock of hair caught.

As I left my mark on it,
It leaves its own on me.
Unharnessed I'm walked away limping,
A fire burns in my front left leg's knee.

Off they take me, who knows where?
And I ask myself do you really care?
All my life spent slaving for tourists!
In the modern world animals are defiantly the poorest!

Ruth Perkins (13)

FUTURE VOICES

When I was a child
I used to run and play.
I used to love the telly,
I could watch it all day.
But then I went to playschool,
I hated it a lot,
The bikes were too small for me,
I couldn't ride them a lot.
I used to like fire,
It kept me nice and warm.

But when I grow up
I won't go to school.
When I grow up
I won't get told off.
When I grow up
I'll lose my hair.
When I grow up
I'll be a millionaire.
I'll have a flashy, fast car
When I grow up.

What I am now is something in between,
Some people say I'm in my teens.
But what I think is, I'm young and free
With not too much responsibility.
I can go and play,
But won't have to work.
I go to school and not to work,
What am I now?

Thomas Gladwin (12)
The Bishops Stortford High School

FUTURE VOICES

Back when I was younger
We would chase around the playground,
Skipping or running
All day long,
Without a care in the world.
Truth or dare?
Live, or let die?
Stuck in the mud or family it?
Playing games all day
Without a care in the world.

When I'm an adult
We will run around an office,
Typing or shouting
All day long,
Worrying about everything possible.
Tuesday's deadline?
Meeting with the boss?
Recruiting or firing or the monthly report?
Working all day
With every worry in the world.

But I'm stuck in the middle,
Trouble at school,
Writing at school or writing at home,
All week long
Not knowing what to do.
Angry teacher?
Greasy hair?
Spotty skin and yesterday's girlfriend,
Homework, skateboard, Friday's disco,
Not knowing what to do.

Alexander Ratcliffe (12)
The Bishops Stortford High School

FUTURE VOICES

When I was a child, I wanted to be *big,*
I piled up cushions and sat on top.
I hid under the dining table
Pretending to be a lion.
When I went to the swimming pool
I pretended to be 'Sharky and George.'
When I was a child I had imaginary friends
And called them nonsense names.
When I played with teddy bears,
I threw them up and tried to catch them again.

When I'm an adult, I can drive a car,
I can visit a pub or go to a bar.
I will be able to vote for my local MP,
And go to university.
Then I'll get a job and earn a big wage
To pay for a pension in my old age.
I'll buy a house, or maybe a flat,
With plenty of room for a dog or a cat.
Maybe I'll marry a beautiful wife,
And together we will have a wonderful life.

Today I like computer games
With amazing graphics.
Everything with high technology, I
Like to find out about.
Various books I like to read, with
Exciting, twisting storylines.
Piano and clarinet are my instruments,
Learning takes plenty of practice.
Useful objects I make in DT.
Sci-fi I watch on TV.

Chris Fleming (12)
The Bishops Stortford High School

FUTURE VOICES

When I was a child, I used to love my nappy,
Playing with my turtle always made me happy,
My mum was everything to me, my happiness, my life,
And when she called out 'dinnertime', I'd collect my yellow knife,
Skittles were the sweeties that I used to like,
Going out and falling off my brand new BMX bike,
Cuts and bruises, crying, walking home with mum in the rain,
Half a day at school, then home for lunch again,
I remember watching 'Thunderbirds' and all the turtles too,
And getting myself all worked up, when locked inside the loo.

But when I am an adult, I'll try hard to earn a wage,
Help my kids when they're young and even at my age,
And hopefully when I've saved up, I'll have my dream sports car,
I'll cruise it down to work and back with a full tank of four star,
No more school, no more teachers, now I'm completely free,
But now I've got to earn a wage, pay tax, electricity fee,
A whole lot of things will change for me; I'll have beers and strength
and hair,
And will I make an idiot of myself and will I actually care?
And money, money, will I spend it, will I have enough or not?
Now I have responsibility, will I lose the plot?

Now my situation is stuck between the two,
Teenage years mean stress for me, what am I going to do?
No time to think, my life moves so fast,
Yet I still find time to think back to the past,
The future though seems one big dream,
I want to play football, but for a decent team,
And building up to GCSE,
Still wondering about university,
Child or adult my life still passes by,
At my age you get into trouble, but God only knows why.

Craig Whyte (12)
The Bishops Stortford High School

FUTURE VOICES

Now I am an adult

Now I am an adult things are not what they used to be.
I'm not drinking fizzy drinks anymore,
I'm drinking tea.

I used to be playing 'bang, bang wars' in the playground,
Now I'm faxing clients for documents to be found!

Oh how I miss this, no Father Christmas,
But I get a card from my parents,
A few presents from my relatives.

Now I am a teenager

Now I am a teenager I don't know who I am,
I'm definitely not a child but I'm also sure that I am.

In my terrible teens,
I don't eat my greens,
I try to look important
And to get the slouch in my walk right.

As I try to cope with sports and such
It reminds me,
How I miss being a child so much.

When I was a child

When I was a child I thought I could fly,
Got other people into trouble,
Then they used to cry!

I would sleep in the afternoon,
Sleep in the morning,
But paddy at night,
Because it was boring!

Girls were from a different planet,
Teachers too,
I used to hate nursery,
I bet I made the teachers hate it too!

Iain Daley (13)
The Bishops Stortford High School

FUTURE VOICES

As a child I always disliked school,
I hated it so much every morning I was sick,
I couldn't wait to go home and get some sweets.
Then I went home to take the dogs out,
Every day round the same walk,
At the same time.

As an adult I'll need to be more responsible,
I won't have to go to school,
Instead it will be work.
I want to be a palaeontologist,
Or a barrister.
I will be rich with no worries apart from if my Ferrari is clean.

So back to my average life,
Not being able to do things but still having fun,
No responsibilities,
No going back to my old life.
But at the end of this day,
I'll be further forward towards my adult life.

Daniel Titheradge (12)
The Bishops Stortford High School

FUTURE VOICES

When I was a child
I loved 'Teenage Mutant Turtles'.
I thought I was one of them,
Fighting Shredder and his men.

Life was easy,
No homework, no worries.
Playgroup was fun
And school was exciting.

'Captain Scarlet' and the 'Thunderbirds',
'Trumpton' and the 'Playbus',
These were the best years.
He ya! Choo, choo Thomas.

But when I am an adult
I will be different.
Full of sophistication,
No more dos or parties.

When I am an adult I don't know what I'll be,
A journalist, a doctor or maybe an MP.

I may start a family,
Two children or three.
Taxes will become common
And I will drive a car.

But at this moment I'm stuck.
Am I an adult?
Am I a child?
Do I want a girlfriend?

Life is not as easy
As it was as a young boy.
Worries and problems
But I'm not an adult yet! Phew!

I consider myself a teenager,
I'm quite mature.
My teenage years have just begun,
I hope it will be fun.

Peter Thompson (12)
The Bishops Stortford High School

FUTURE VOICES

When I was a child
I thought girls were yucky,
I would jump on my mum and dad's bed,
I would make forts out of our sheets,
I would climb the tree in the garden.

When I am an adult
I will be free from school,
I will boss people about,
I will stay up late,
I will play computer games,
I will rent out loads of new films.

Now I am a teenager
Life is a drag,
Girls are more interesting,
You've got to act cool,
Get the latest haircut and clothes,
Hang about at night,
Now I'm a teenager, life's boring.

Lawrence Hayes (12)
The Bishops Stortford High School

FUTURE VOICES

When I was a child I was small,
I looked up at my dad and felt like a fool.
When I was a child I was full of cheek,
I often wet my nappy because of a leak.
When I was a child I was silly,
I ran around naked and free roamed my wi . . .!

When I'm an adult, I'll be even stronger,
I'll be taller, harder and my body will be even longer!
I'll have a fast car to drive independently away,
Into the sun for the rest of the day.

Now I'm a teenager and I've hit puberty,
I'm bigger, hairier and I look normally.
My hormones play up, it's been a hard day,
I've got to get through this, one or another way!

Fabio Poma (12)
The Bishops Stortford High School

FUTURE VOICES

When I was young, I'd cry and suck on my thumb,
When I was young, I'd throw up on my mum!
When I was young, I was scared of the dark,
When I was young, I loved going to the park.
When I was young, it was the best.

When I'm an adult, I'll stay out all night,
When I'm an adult, I'll act very bright!
When I'm an adult, I'll rent out eighteen movies,
When I'm an adult, I'll have my own house and keys.

Now I'm a teenager, girls are more attractive,
Now I'm a teenager, I'm a lot more active.
Now I'm a teenager, I'm more ugly,
Now I'm a teenager, I've gone all spotty.
Now I'm a teenager, life's a *drag!*

Dean Gunn (13)
The Bishops Stortford High School

FUTURE VOICES

When I was a child
I'd build forts on my bed,
My older brother was my very best friend,
I dressed up in costumes, I'd laugh and laugh,
Sometimes I was naughty, I threw clothes in the bath.

When I'm an adult
I'll get lots of mail,
I'll have to go to work early,
My stocks will rise and fall,
I might become an old fogey,
Playing golf and getting par, birdies and bogies.

But for now I'm a teenager,
Seemingly stuck between the two,
Some people call me a young adult,
Some call me a child (which I rue),
My mother says, 'Now you're older, watch for acne.'
So I guess that a teenager I should be,
But no matter how people expect me to act,
I'll always just try to be me.

Matthew Eggleston (13)
The Bishops Stortford High School

FUTURE VOICES

When I was a child I made a mess,
I hardly ever sat down to rest,
Half eaten chocolate bars on the floor,
Vomit all over every door,
Every toy I had I would break,
My mum would say, 'For goodness sake!
Why break your toys? They're brand new.
Why try to flush Action Man down the loo.'
My mum started not to buy me new stuff,
She would just say, 'That's tough.'

When I am an adult things won't be like now,
Buildings will be raised off the ground,
Then I would be more mature,
Because we're adults in the future.
I could be a fireman, a builder or a cop,
Maybe a rugby player, playing prop.
Who could be Prime Minister? Who could it be,
Tony Blair, William Hague or even me?

Now I am doing alright,
I'm trying to complete a game on my Dreamcast, which I soon might,
Now I have my own boat,
My garage is packed full of different sizes of rope.
I like sailing, I like it a lot.
It's better than my mum's interest of china pots.
Some people don't like me,
But as long as I'm happy, that's my cup of tea.

William Mead (12)
The Bishops Stortford High School

FUTURE VOICES

When I was a baby I used to jump in the swimming pool
and make a huge splash because I did not want to get in slowly.

When I was a baby I liked the chewy mushrooms in the sweet mix so
I picked those out and didn't eat the others.

When I was a baby I was so excited about opening a square on the
Advent calendar and eating the chocolate that I sucked the chocolate
to make it last longer.

When I am an adult I shall stay up late and eat popcorn
because I can't stay up late and I love popcorn.

When I am an adult I shall play computer games
after I get in from work because I never have time after school.

When I am an adult I shall do loads of wheelies and stunts
on my bike because I'm not allowed to now.

Now I am a teenager, I hate going to bed at night but
want to stay in bed in the morning.

Now I am a teenager, I get stressed at exams - I hate that.
Always worrying whether you will do well or not.

Now I am a teenager, I always have loads of homework when
I get home and no TV like I did when I was a baby.

Lyndon Bird (12)
The Bishops Stortford High School

FUTURE VOICES

When I was a child
I screamed at nursery school.
On a cold winter's day when I had the flu
I snuggled up in a ball and watched 'Spot The Dog'.
I liked to go to the park and play on the swing,
When my gran came round we used to play, dance and sing.

When I am an adult
And I have a wife,
A son and two daughters,
I am working as a barrister at the Old Bailey court,
Then I will look back at my nursery schooldays
When I am sitting in my chair drinking my wine,
I will wish I am a child.

Now I am a teen
In my school age days,
Rugby on a Saturday, football on a Sunday.
All I do is play sport
But girls are coming in;
The strawberry blondes and brunettes,
These are the new interests,
The big problem is *spots!*

How do I get rid of them?
All I will do is wait.

Paul Clark (12)
The Bishops Stortford High School

FUTURE VOICES

When I was a child I would stand on my dad's foot and hold his leg,
He would take me around the huge house,
I would sit in my room in front of the bars,
When someone came past I would run my beaker along the bars,
The only other activities were holding my dad's leg and eating,
Running from one end of the sofa to another, seemed to take ages.

When I'm an adult I'll do what's safe,
I'll do my job and help the poor,
I'll give the church a lot, lot more.
When I'm older I'll help Mum,
I'll help my dad.
When I'm an adult I'll get married,
I'll have two kids,
I'll keep them happy,
My sisters will not have to worry,
Hopefully I'll be able to give them money.

As I enter my teenage years I find life hard and lots of fear,
SATs are near but yet so far,
When I look back in the past,
It has gone so very fast,
I wish I could be back there now,
But I've still got my life to go.

Alex Oldfield (12)
The Bishops Stortford High School

FUTURE VOICES

When I was a child I'd be sleeping with my mum,
I would suck my thumb,
With chips in my mouth.
When I was a child I'd kick my dog,
Stamp on the floor and cry.
When I was a child I'd dribble my drink,
Wipe it on my shirt,
With beans on the floor.
When I was a child I'd run around naked
Hoping my mum would dress me.

When I am an adult I'd go in my car,
Go anywhere, drinking beer.
When I am an adult I will get married
And have a child with a beautiful woman.
When I am an adult I'd get lots of money,
Get a good job which will be very funny.
When I am an adult I'd go nightclubs.
Will I do what I hope to do?

Now as I enter my teenage years,
I want to go to university and study chemistry.
As you may have guessed I have many fears
As I enter my teenage years.
Time is going very fast,
I look back to my dazzling past.
SATs are near but yet too far,
I'm very nervous, un, deux, trois.
Will I get a really good job?
Get lots of money or be a slob?

Josh Simpson (12)
The Bishops Stortford High School

FUTURE VOICES

When I was a child
I'd race all day,
With my super cars
It was Formula One every day.
I'd cry and shout and scream and wheel,
'There goes Mansell followed by Hill!'

Then at school I lived to play
With my tiny friends,
We worshipped chase, *oweea, oweea!*

When I'm an adult
There will be no one in my way,
Eighteen movies,
Rest, relax and a huge pay day!

I'll live on pizza,
I'll have PlayStation 3,
I'll subscribe to a magazine,
I'll have to work . . .
All day!

Caught between the two,
I suffer all day,
More and more homework,
Maths every other day!

Fun is gone,
Almost anyway,
I'll still have my PlayStation,
And spot cream, *ooohi!*

Andrew Lewin (12)
The Bishops Stortford High School

FUTURE VOICES

When I was a child
I put slugs in my bed.
I rolled in spilt custard
With pants on my head!
I ran around naked
And pulled down my shorts.
Got stuck in a dustbin
And learned how to talk.
I was scared of big clocks that went tick and went tock,
I cuddled my mummy and peed in my socks!

When I'm a grown-up
I'll lead a new life.
I'll have to pay bills
And I might have a wife!
I'll spend all my days
In an office or in banks,
And pay lots of taxes
To make lots of tanks!
When I am seventy I'll get rather slow,
And wish till I die I was eighteen or so!

Who am I now?
Stuck with toy tanks,
Teddies, computers,
Accounts in a bank.
I'm stuck in the middle,
I'm misunderstood,
I've been turned upside-down,
Bad is now good.
How will I cope with the stuff that's to come?
I'll just have to wait until I'm twenty-one!

Nicholas Cork (12)
The Bishops Stortford High School

FUTURE VOICES

When I was a child
I'd play hide and seek,
I'd put cushions on the floor
and jump from one to the other,
just like the man on ITV.
When I went shopping with Mum or Dad
I always put sweets in the trolley
and they would never see!

When I am an adult
I can do what I want.
I can jump on the sofa
with no one to say, 'No!'
When I am an adult
I can eat what I want including
fish and chips every night!
If I ever become an adult
I just can't wait!

Soon I'll be a teenager,
my parents are dreading that!
They say I'll get spots and be ugly,
(I'll never be ugly).
I'll also be able to drink when
I'm eighteen . . . yes!

Sam Hunt (12)
The Bishops Stortford High School

FUTURE VOICES

When I was a child
I dreamt about flying every night,
I always wanted a car to get out of sight.
When I was a child
'Sonic the Hedgehog' was my best show,
My brother went to school, I always wanted to go.
When I was a child
I used to play pirates in the big green garden,
When it was bedtime I used to die of boredom,
When I was a child!

When I am an adult
I'll say to myself:
At last school is over,
I've passed my driving test, might get the new Rover.
Now the bills, cheques, insurance come pouring in,
I'll get so stressed I'll throw them in the bin.
When I am an adult,
I also will think to myself,
As the days go past and it's going to be hard to bend,
Every day that goes past is going to be nearer to the end.

My life is now difficult and getting much harder,
The exams come near, I feel nervous and much sadder.
As well as school the family is very stressing,
My brother shouting at me when I haven't done anything.
I'm not thirteen yet but will be on the 15th December,
Being thirteen I'm going to have all these to remember:
Exams, family and the responsibilities.
I haven't chosen what to be when I grow up yet, so many possibilities.

Shahim Malik (12)
The Bishops Stortford High School

FUTURE VOICES

When I was a child
I rode on my dog,
He was my army tank.
My base was a duvet over a chair,
If intruders should lurk
Out came the jelly bombs.

When I was a child
Days seemed like years,
When it snowed I would explore.

When I am an adult
My head will be bare,
I'll have my own comfy chair.
I might even have a tie collection
But I can't even have a lie-in!

When I am an adult
My feet will have grown,
But I'll have a house of my own.
The coffee I drink will be
Creamy and thick.

But at the moment
I am not either.
My world is TV
Day and night,
Me versus my family.

Today is tomorrow,
Tomorrow is last year,
Keep up with the trend
And life will be your friend.

Dean Boyle (12)
The Bishops Stortford High School

FUTURE VOICES

When I was a child, I always fell asleep,
When I used to play, I always built a square keep.
When I was a child, I always shouted for a treat,
Usually when I shouted, I usually got beat.
When I was a child, I hated my nappy,
But now I'm a teenager, I am always happy.
When I was a child, I always sucked my thumb,
When I got a cut on my arm, I cried for my mum.
Now that it is Christmas Day,
Here comes Santa on his sleigh.

When I am an adult, I will hang out with girls,
The only bad thing is, I will have to buy them pearls.
When I am an adult, I won't get much sleep,
One good thing is, I won't really weep.
When I am an adult, I will drink loads of beer,
I will hope to see a golden deer.
When I am an adult, I'll take my son to the zoo,
And I will buy him a grey and black dog, but I won't clean up its poo.

Now I enter teenage years,
I sneak down a couple of beers.
Now I am a teenager I will play on my computer,
My favourite game at the moment is 'Mutter'.
Now I'm a teenager life is going fast,
And now I look back into my dazzling past.
Now I'm a teenager, I've got a hairy chest,
Hanging and pulling girls is what I do best.

Jack Webb (12)
The Bishops Stortford High School

FUTURE VOICES

When I was a child
I thought I was a hero,
I played with guns and swords, with a damsel in distress.
I was not embarrassed when naked,
Nor when I had all the attention.
I did not think as much as I do now,
Nor did I know what I know now!
I could stay awake till half past eleven
And eat sweets, whenever I wanted, 5, 6 or 7.
As I think about my childhood, I see nothing but happiness,
But now, as I grow older, I see more and more sadness in life.

I'm in adulthood now,
I won't have to go to school!
Instead I go to work.
When I'm older I hope to marry,
To have company as I age,
And to have dinner in a posh restaurant,
And pay with my own money.
I will soon be able to drive a car
And go to clubs, drinking champagne,
But will it be so easy, or will it be much harder?

As I lie on my bed one night
I think to myself, who am I?
Am I a child, a teenager or an adult?
Can I do the things I want yet?
Have all the teddies gone out of my range?
Have I got spots to show my age
Or am I involved with girls more and more?
Some may say I'm a teenager or child,
Whatever they say I'm not sure myself . . .

Alexander Chan (12)
The Bishops Stortford High School

FUTURE VOICES

When I was a child
I'd cry and cry for something I'd want that someone else had,
I'd just go mad,
I'd chew everything I could see from a wriggly worm to my cuffs
and my sleeves,
When I came home from school I'd make a great fort
On the floor of my room, a colourful assort,
I'd dress up in costumes of turtles and co,
And make a great snowman when it would snow.

When I am an adult,
I'll lose all my hair,
I'll go to the caves where no one else dares,
I'll own a big house by The Nile,
And look back on my life as a child,
I'll have a good job as a pilot,
I might have to go on a diet,
I'll have a nice car like a Merc,
And go and show it off at work.

As I'm stuck between the two worlds,
I don't know when I'm coming or going,
I can still do some things but not others,
I still play with sisters and brothers,
I still play with toys but more grown-up like
TVs and PlayStations.
Do I want to be young or want to be old?
As I mature I'm sure I'll be told.

Adam Lunn (12)
The Bishops Stortford High School

THEN, WHEN AND NOW

Afraid of the shadows under the duvet I'd hide
Then come up for air with my eyes open wide.
Noise, like toilets flushing, would give me a fright
And other strange sounds in the dead of the night.
I made up silly ways of walking up stairs,
Life was so simple without any cares.
Watching TV, I thought the man was inside,
My parents said no, but I thought they lied.

As an adult I'll enjoy doing my own thing,
I'll have fun staying up late partying,
Finding the right job will be a test,
But whatever I'll do I'll give it my best.
I'll be able to go on holiday just with friends
It'll be so good, I'll wish it never ends.
Learning to drive a car will be so cool
And best of all not having to go to school.

Now, I'm in the in between years,
Dealing with all my hopes and fears.
I still like to play with my childish toys
And love to play out with the rest of the boys.
Schoolwork and homework take so much of my time,
I just want to have fun, not make things rhyme,
I don't want to grow up, but I know it must come,
I just want to stay home with my dad and my mum.

Mark Graves (12)
The Bishops Stortford High School

BOY OR MAN

When I was a kid,
I used to wear a bib
And couldn't help but fib.
When I was a kid
I used to build tree houses
But never caught the buses,
Instead I went to town on rocking horses.
When I'm an adult
I'm going to get drunk,
And might even become a punk.
When I'm an adult,
I'll drive fast cars,
God knows, I might even go to Mars.
But am I an adult or a little child?
Can I rent 12s or 18s?
Should I hide from monsters under the bed?
I don't know, am I a man or a mouse?

Daniel Chinn (12)
The Bishops Stortford High School

WHEN I WAS A CHILD

When I was a child I would suck my thumb,
When I look back it seems really dumb.
I have a best friend and he was called Norwich,
He used to *love* his hot bowl of porridge.

When I am a teenager I want to be a punk,
I want to be a wrestler and be called, 'Billy Slam Dunk'.
I want to drive a moped and drive around town,
When I come to a hill I'd just go down, down, down.

When I am an adult I want to drive a fast car,
All my best friends would be hanging around in bars.
I would live on my own in a cosy, nice flat,
I would probably buy a lovely furry old cat.

But I'm stuck between *all* three, nothing to do
But when I'm bored I just go to zzzzz.
In these few years of my life I'll spend time with my mum
Because she's really nice, she fills up my tum.

Howard Teall (12)
The Bishops Stortford High School

GROWING UP

When I was a child . . .

When I was a child, I'd cry and cry for no reason,
I'd play with my toys, I'd be near to my mum,
I'd wear clashing clothes and have messy hair,
I'd dribble on my bib and the carpet.

When I am an adult . . .

When I am an adult I can drive like a maniac,
I could stop off at night clubs and break rank and have a ball,
I could teach and be boring,
I could study and do drawing, but I'd rather be just normal.

How I am now . . .

Now as I enter my teenage years,
I'm looking forward to enjoying my driving years,
I'm trying to forget about tests and exams
And drinking with friends and saying 'cheers.'

Sean Merry (12)
The Bishops Stortford High School

YOUR AGE

When I was a child
I played kiss chase
And always entered the school race.
As I turned out the light with a fright
I would wake up in the middle of the night.
I would slide down my stairs in the morn
Also I slid down it at dawn.

When I am an adult
I will drive fast cars
Going down to the local bars.
Having my own house,
The only thing is cleaning out my house
And having my favourite iced buns
And best of all having fun.

Caught between the two.
When I was a child they called me small,
When now I am an adult they call me tall.
I went from sitting in those little cots
Now I have lots of spots.

William Tonkin (12)
The Bishops Stortford High School

MY AGE POEM

When I was a child . . .
I did lots of silly things
Like playing 'kiss chase',
Jumping off high things.
I thought TV was real,
I couldn't sleep at night,
I hung over the banisters afraid of the night.
I played with baby toys and was scared of silly things.

When I am an adult . . .
I will drive a fast car and play music loud,
I might even stand out in a party crowd.
I will drink all night and have loads of fun,
But hang on, what about the responsibilities?
I have to work for my food and a bed to sleep in,
I pay taxes and get overwhelmed with responsibilities,
Well, maybe being an adult isn't so great.

What about now? I'm right in between.
What should I do, what can I do?
Adults don't listen and children misunderstand,
What will happen tomorrow, or next year?
Will I get hurt, will I be able to fly?
How should I know, I'm still very young.

James Tomlinson (12)
The Bishops Stortford High School

A POEM ABOUT ME GROWING UP

When I was a baby, I'd sleep all day,
But by night, I'd scream the hours away.
I loved my milk, all I could get,
My mum said my nappies were always wet.

Teddy Toes was my best chum,
We'd have a cuddle, I'd suck my thumb.
When I was naughty he'd help me out,
'It was Teddy Toes, not me!' I used to shout.

When I was four Mum gave me a brother
And he was a pal like there's no other.
Like Teddy Toes, he'd take the blame
But once he could talk, it wasn't the same.

He'd always argue and say it was me,
But I'm four years older, so how could that be?
He touches my things and makes me wild!
He can be such a noisy, annoying child.

Now that I'm older, it's all doom and gloom,
'Do your homework, tidy your room.
Look after your brother, help more round the house.
Don't make so much noise, be quiet as a mouse.'

But what am I saying, I don't really mind,
My mum is the best, she's loving and kind.
She drives me around, has friends back to tea,
She helps with my problems and listens to me.

When I get older, it won't be so bad,
I hope I'll be just like my mum and my dad!

Andrew Wells (12)
The Bishops Stortford High School

CHANGING TIMES

When I was small, my elders were giants,
I'd create a base from the sofa,
I'd check for snakes in my bed,
I'd check for a lurking bogeyman,
I'd know they were there,
just not when I stare,
Shadows were real,
TV was just another world,
Well, that's what I was told,
Santa was true, as was Winnie the Pooh,
Friends were friends in the morning,
Enemies in the afternoon and
Friends again next morning,
Those were the days.

When I'm an adult I'll be free,
I'll have lots of beer,
no longer have fear,
My life will be clear,
yet it won't be as free as it's said to be,
Responsibilities are high,
People will die,
And you'll still have to do up your tie,
But those'll be the days.

But now I'm here,
Caught in the middle,
You're childish if you play,
Pretending if you're sensible,
And you don't know what to do,
But these are the days which I once said
'Those'll be the days.'

Tim Akers (12)
The Bishops Stortford High School

WHEN I WAS YOUNG

Being a child is not so bad,
Actually it's quite fun, playing Action Men,
Sliding downstairs (ow!)
But when you get scared it's a real fright,
Checking under your bed for the bogie man,
Then hiding under the covers perfectly still (ssshhhhh).

But when I'm an adult things get fun!
Think of the freedom
Having parties, having money,
Buying fast cars and no homework - yes!
But I suppose going to work seven days a week
Cannot be as fun,
Paying taxes,
Paying bills!
Getting stressed
And taking pills! Noooooo.

What about now though?
Will I get my GCSEs?
Will I get a good job?
Will I live to a ripe old age?
Or will the world just end?

Geoffrey Bunton (13)
The Bishops Stortford High School

WHEN I WAS A CHILD

When I was a child
I could go outside and play
And whenever I played 'kiss chase'
The girls just ran away.

But now I am an adult,
I can't go out and play,
And whenever I play 'kiss chase'
the girls just say 'way hay.'

Even though I'm older,
I'd love to be so young,
'Cause when you're so much younger,
You can have so much fun.

The troubles that I have,
Oh how I hate them so,
Divorces, taxes and so on,
They never let me go.

But when I was a child
I could run around all day,
The only problem that I had
Was 'What's for dinner today?'

Gary Harman (12)
The Bishops Stortford High School

MY POEM

When I was a child,
I remember dreaming of terrifying monsters,
Constantly hiding under the covers.
I remember the bright lights
Shining through the windows
And the songs of the birds every morning.
I remember all the little figures and toys
I played with,
And the little presents my mum gave me.
I remember the little tree I once planted.

When I am an adult,
The little tree is finally big,
Now I am not the small, little one,
But now I have more worries,
Like money and bills.

Who am I now?
I sit at home as time passes by,
Almost in my teens.
Homework's getting harder,
But school's much more fun.
I'm now off to enjoy myself
With a game of football.
As I close my eyes at night,
I start to dream once again.

Robert Helps (12)
The Bishops Stortford High School

WHEN I WAS A CHILD

When I was a child, there were many silly things I did.
I used to be afraid of things, like dragons, that didn't exist,
And acting all weird just to attract other people's attention.
I used to play with toys that are now considered 'uncool',
Like Thomas The Tank Engine, Lego and Playmobile.
At school, I would run around screaming my head off,
Collecting stones and making bases in the trees in the woods.
But, when I was a child, I was not taken as seriously as I wanted to be.

I hope all that will change when I am an adult.
I want to be respected and loved by my family and friends
And start taking life more seriously than I have been doing previously.
I don't want to make a fool of myself by drinking and driving,
Or disobey the law in any harmful way.
I want to make use of my life, enjoy it to the full,
Do what I can with my life and leave my mark on the world.

At the moment though, I don't know where I am.
I'm bang smack in the middle, somewhere in between.
My role is to set an example to younger people
And to make that adult future possible.
It is also to have fun and make friends and do interesting things,
But I also want to be careful and not do anything I'll regret later in life.
I want to have fun, I want to be free,
I'll come to the future when it comes to me.

Oliver Short (12)
The Bishops Stortford High School

MY LIFE

When I was a child,
I did lots of silly things like
Jumping off the stairs, getting higher and higher.
Having that special teddy that went everywhere you went,
Hiding under the covers, afraid of the shadows.
Pedal cars that you raced around in like F1 cars.

When I am an adult,
I can have a fast car to race around in and have really loud music,
Have parties all night long,
The alcohol that you can't stop drinking,
Having loads of money that you can spend on anything,
No parents to tell you what to do.

But now I am caught between the two,
I think about what job I am going to get,
No one to look after you, no one to cook for you,
But then I think about marriage, I could get married and my wife
                                                    could cook.

Simon Wells (11)
The Bishops Stortford High School

AS TIME GOES BY

When I was a child,
I used to be scared of anything,
From the flush of the toilet
To things on the TV.
I used to do silly things,
Like playing 'kiss chase'
And slide down the stairs at 100 mph.

When I am older,
I will have a mad craving
To listen to music as loud as my ears will let me,
And try dodgy things, like cigarettes and drugs
And the occasional tyre burn-out.

But right now, all I can say and think is
I can't wait till I grow up!

Salvatore Russo (12)
The Bishops Stortford High School

STAGES OF LIFE

When I was little, I could be afraid;
When you're big, you must be brave.
I used to be afraid of shadows at night;
When you're big, you must be intelligent and bright.

When you're big, you can drive fast cars,
When you're little, all you drive are pedal cars.
When you're big, you can spend loads of money,
When you're little, you find everything funny!

Now I'm at a confusing age.
Am I big or am I small?
Or am I neither, not mattering at all?

Ben Bishop (12)
The Bishops Stortford High School

GROWING UP - CONFUSED? YOU WILL BE!

When I was a young boy,
I used to laugh and cry,
I used to ask so many questions -
'Why? Why? Why?'

I used to be scared of the dark
Have a light in my bed,
My dad would come and turn it off
When I was asleep, resting my sleepy head.

I used to splash the water every time I had a bath,
you could see that I had no teeth
Every time I laughed.

After I had dried off from my bath,
I would fall asleep in my mother's arms,
Then she would put me into bed
And sing to me - 'Rest your sleepy head.'

When I am an adult,
I want to learn to drive,
I want to get married,
Keep fit for the rest of my life.

I want to be a rich man
And be pleasant with it as well,
I want someone to pick me up
Whenever I fall.

At the moment, I'm stuck in the middle,
Not knowing what I want to do.
Sometimes I'm confident with my work,
Sometimes I haven't a clue.

I am two different people at the same time,
Depending on who is speaking.
I can't wait to be a man,
Clever, witty, I think I can.

Richard Judge (12)
The Bishops Stortford High School

MY LIFE

When I was young I'd fly up high,
Or fight off scary monsters with a clown's custard pie!
Whatever I needed my mum made mine,
From a seven-ton elephant to a ride on the Rhine.
When I was young, my life was fine.

When I'm an adult I'll stay out all night
And drive my fast cars till I see the daylight.
I'll dance to the funk, even dress like a punk
And no one can say, 'I'll not allow that, no way.'

But now, I'm in the middle
And my life is one big muddle
And I feel my problems will never go away,
Until that great fine day,
When an adult big and strong I will be.

Nick McCowan (13)
The Bishops Stortford High School

AGES

When I was young
I had hours of fun,
Playing war games,
Calling people names,
Making a cool base,
Calling it my special place,
Roaring round the block on my tricycle,
Can't wait to ride a bicycle.

When I'm an adult,
I'll drive a fast car,
Pump up the volume on my electric guitar.
Staying up all night,
No one can tell me what to do,
I can even go out with only one shoe.
Going on holiday with all of my friends,
Free as a bird, the fun will never end.

In the middle is such a drag,
You're not one or the other,
Your mum still sees you as a little boy,
Tucking you in under your cover.
Feeling young and having fun
While the adult in me wants to slow down.
Why do we have to be in such a position
When all I want to do is hide under the covers,
Wishing my problems away.

Matthew Groves (12)
The Bishops Stortford High School

LITTLE ACORNS OF LOVE

Peace and love, wonderful love,
Perfect peace, sound of the heart,
Beating, beating,
In tribute to you
Thoughts of tenderness.

Waves of water cascading,
Cleansing lovingly
All the parts
That have been hurt.

Be kind, precious,
Rest your weary heart.
Love grows as the day goes by,
It is special to us.

Just listen, you will hear
A melody of love.

Out of a little acorn an oak tree grows,
When you plant a seed of love,
A fab flower grows.

So when you plant seeds, don't sow discontent,
Sow happiness and praise and love,
Then your oak tree will be watered from above
And filled with tender, true love.

Emma Poulter (14)
Freman College

HORROR

In your dreams at night,
You're in for a horrible scare,
All out in your screaming terror and fright,
A satanic supernatural despair,
It turns your blood into a foamy froth,
It turns you into stone,
A vampire's dinner of jugular broth,
A zombie's curdling groan,
A shadow of an altered beast,
A pale victim's corpse,
A body with no hands or feet,
A psycho with no remorse.
The devil is inside a poor girl's head,
A demonic human possession,
We'll have the spirit solely dead,
This satanic monster's obsession.
We'll exorcise the ghostly reminiscence,
This poltergeist will leave,
We'll chase away this spiritual presence,
A reaper's right to reave.

Louis Dyke (14)
Freman College

LIFE AND DEATH

Life is lying on a beach - and getting sand in your eyes,
Life is enjoying a hot bath - and becoming wrinkled,
Life is riding on a roller-coaster - and being sick afterwards,
Life is eating ten ice-creams - and then worrying about being fat,
Life is having relationships - and being jealous of friends.
Life.
Don't worry about it - it happens to all of us.

Death is lying in a box - and being placed under the ground,
Death is enjoying peace - but not knowing that it exists,
Death is riding on a wave - and being washed up with the sewage,
Death is being unable to eat - but being eaten,
Death is having no worries - nor anything to look forward to.
Death.
Don't worry about it - it happens to all of us.

Elizabeth West (15)
Freman College

THE MEETING PLACE

The derelict church tower stood bleak in the moonlight,
It was midnight,
The clock struck twelve,
The bats fluttered from the tower,
An owl hooted in the distance,
A vixen screeched for her mate,
A dark figure emerged from behind a headstone.
The man, waiting alone, went towards it
Thinking it was his beloved,
It drifted slowly towards the church door,
A black cloud covered the moon,
The figure seemingly vanished through the church door.
The young man felt the hair on the back of his neck
Stand on end,
Where had she gone?
It began to rain,
Looking for his love,
He tried the door.
It was locked.

Victoria Pitt (14)
Freman College

GROWTH

On the brink of the hill stands an ancient worn cross
Marking the grave of forgotten old souls,
As the mist rises off the arms of the oak
It stands sparse and cold,
Dead except for the moss that climbs up its trunk,
Majestic and old.
Standing together they look over the hill
And watch as the weather rolls through,
As the fog in the valley blends the gnarled pair
Their features are of one, not of two.

If isolation is the state of this civilised world
Then our future can't be too bright,
But if we all pull together, use our knowledge and love,
We can tackle the problems in sight.
When we can help others come in from the cold
And stand together as one,
We'll be like the pair on the top of the hill,
Be proud, majestic and old.
If the world can be honest, have peace and not war
And it can be passed down the line,
Then our children will grow in a happy, free world,
We've just given that little bit more.

Lauren Porter (14)
Freman College

THIS WORLD OF MINE

If the world was mine, I'd no longer be its prisoner,
If dreams were real, nightmares could be forgotten.

So many detailed things change a person's life, momentarily,
So many simple things change mankind forever.

In the past, the future was rosy, now we're here it's just bleak.
In tomorrow's world, days will turn to nights
And pure sunshine will be a possession that is no longer mankind's.

When people are young, they wish to be old.
When people grow old, they wish they'd stayed young.
Will technology continue to rule, or will the mind regain its lead?
Will men of a different origin, ever be seen the same?

Many people see what they want to see and not what should be seen,
Many people glance once at things that should be studied.

A snack can seem a feast to someone who is starved,
A day can seem a lifetime for someone unjustly imprisoned.

There is no end of time, unless time had a beginning,
There is no meaning to happiness, unless you've faced perfect misery.

Without war, peace would not be known
Without hate, the world would only know love.

Tina Nutt (14)
Freman College

HORROR

The dark skies cover the graveyard,
Everything is silent,
The wind scatters the leaves
With its whispers in the breeze.

Tonight the moon is full,
What will happen next?
Will it be the sight of death,
Or the smell of unbearable breath?

Horror is your worst fear,
Worse than a nightmare,
It's an obsession of fright,
Deep within the night.

Some would call it poison,
Unexplained and twisted,
No one really knows,
But the venom really shows.

Horror's around the corner,
You can sense it in the air,
Horror's around the corner,
Quick, get out, it's there.

Lauren McBride (14)
Freman College

WHAT TO BE, OR WHAT NOT TO BE?

What do I want to be?
I've been asked thousands of times.
Everybody else seems to know,
But I don't.
Do I want to be a butcher,
Or a sailor on the sea?
I'm a vegetarian, I can't swim.
Do I want to be a teacher,
Or the pilot of a plane?
I hate children, I'm afraid of heights.
Do I want to be a bomb disposer,
Cutting that little red wire?
That job isn't for me, I'm colour-blind.
Do I want to be a florist,
Or a surgeon in a hospital?
I have hayfever, I'm very squeamish.
Do I want to be a taxi driver,
Or a zoo keeper with arachnids?
I get travel-sick, I'm scared of spiders.
So what do I want to be?
I guess I'm just stuck with being
Me.

Jenny Castle (14)
Freman College

TECHNOLOGY

People aren't required,
Computers control all,
We live under technology's watchful eye.

Dying has been prevented,
Dying is not an option, we are immortal slaves
Technology is our remorseless god.

Entertainment has become outlawed,
Actors gone, dancers gone, singers gone,
No one lives to fulfil a dream any more.

There is no need for mankind,
There is no use in living,
We created it, it ruined us.

Robert Hurst (14)
Freman College

THE DANCING DEAD

It was five past the witching hour,
All was dark, all was cold and damp,
The swirling clouds passed the moon,
The smell of evil was in the air.

The graveyard was the darkest spot,
The rough old gravestones
Stood upright for miles.
The moon shone upon this mysterious sight,
An uneasy feeling drifted through the sky.

Then the tapping started again,
Then a creak, the creak that sends a shiver down your spine.
The tapping grew louder and faster,
A crazy, scary laugh echoed through the night.

Then they rose, ten or more dancing to the wind,
They were bones, waking up the dead,
Some had weapons, some were violent,
Some were dripping blood.
They sang, they danced, they laughed, they cried,
A horrible, deathly sight.

Laurenne Campany (14)
Freman College

SPACE

20 years, human technology leaps ahead,
Lightning transport, different worlds,
Opportunities, chances to see,
See our universe.

Space is wonderful, space is unknown,
Totally different world,
Bright flashes spark through the emptiness,
Exploration of this natural world,
Don't kill it.

Better lifestyles, new planets,
Chances to start over again,
Regenerate, new beginnings,
These strange untouched places,
What will the next 20 years bring?

Chris Buckmaster (14)
Freman College

DESIRE FOR BLOOD

As the night approached,
I made my way past the haunted house.
As I walked up the stony path,
I thought I heard someone's eerie laugh.
At the window, something did appear,
Or was it just I, full of fear?
A gruesome man stepped out in front of me,
He reached for his knife and vanished into thin air.
He had a gloomy look filled with fire,
But his face was as white as ice.
Blood was his desire,
He stayed in my gory nightmares for life.
His teeth were gruesomely deranged,
They were killer teeth, but fiercely arranged.
He reached for my neck and took a bite,
But then it turned seriously light,
And that's the end of my terrible fright.

Kerry Young (14)
Freman College

DREAM ON . . .

Lying in the scorching summer sun,
Huddling in the awful autumn gales,
Sandy beach in Jamaica, relaxing,
Stony beach in Blackpool, 'Wish you were here?'
Sparking champagne and a six-course meal,
Cold coffee and soggy fish 'n' chips.

Melinda Messenger chats to me,
Maggy, the lady next door, moans at night,
Flash, expensive limo, pedigree poodle,
Bashed-up Skoda, unwanted mongrel,
Flying home, chestnut brown,
Walking home, ghostly white.

Mark Lawrenson (14)
Freman College

THE CAR CRASH

Shock, horror, bang, smash,
Just another car crash.

Bodies littered on the road,
Just a lorry overload.

Hands and feet all over the place,
Severed limbs, a piece of face.

The driver's dead, oh what a shame.
To haulage bosses it's just a game.

A money game with a lot of stress,
Who cares that they leave a mess?

People need more money we say,
Bereaved relatives have to pay.

We really must control our greed,
These warnings everyone must heed.

Philip Hamel (14)
Freman College

WHAT IS LIFE?

Life is a challenge,
We need to bear it,
It may be hard,
So simplify it.

Life always leads to death,
Try to face it,
Then all you have to do is
Accept it.

Life always is cruel,
Just overcome it,
Remember,
You can ease it.

Life is boring,
Be happy about it,
Just never
Laugh at it.

Life will always be love,
You will receive it
And always,
Give it.

Life is life,
Just live it.

Natasha Apperley (14)
Freman College

HORROR

V ampires suck blood,
I solated house,
O gres big and bad,
L ethal weapons,
E erie happenings,
N oises in the dark,
T wisted stories.

H orrible faces,
O ozing blood,
R epulsive sights,
R ough voices,
O bsessive monsters,
R uthless murders.

D ecaying bones,
A wful smells,
R evolting,
K nives kill,
N ightmares scary,
E vil spirits,
S pooky witches,
S trange zombies.

Samara Smith (14)
Freman College

LUNAR VISIONS

Moon, cold and desolate.
Isolated cities rarely seen,
Towers tall, watch the ground, far below,
Creatures green are unknown,
Beings wander amidst the covered man,
Silver birds fall from space and conquer the rough, rocky terrain.
Green, blue life, far distant unlike grey of near.
Here I stand, surrounded by this dismal beast.
Future, where do you lead now?
Where will the metal wings take us?
New worlds, new solar systems, new galaxies?
Will we stay here with the comfort of the Earth?
Will *I* stay here with the comfort of the Earth,
Or on the moon so cold and desolate?

Alex Sparrowhawk (14)
Freman College

THE FARM SHEEP

Striped bear in the cold air, the scared old sheep stood alone in the rain.
On top of the hill trampling the grass, a stranger came and called.
It was the farmer who gently picked me up with his warm hands.
With a look as if I was a dog and stared into my eyes.
He moved me to the disused pigsty.
I got placed down all so slow and I was scared and confused.
As like a human I wanted to cry but thought a lonely sigh.
The farmer whispered in his sweet old voice and said
                              he wouldn't hurt me ever.
He said he put me here to keep me warm and dry as I was old
                              and could die not in a sty.
Then I understood he loved me like a dog different from other sheep.

Oliver Seymour (11)
John Warner School

I HAVE A FRIEND

I have a friend who can run like the wind,
She is so fast that you know she will win.
I have a friend who just loves animals.
She has three at home,
But that's not enough.
I have a friend who is really nice,
She is a friend you would like to have.
I have a friend who is so, so tall,
People call her names but I think she's cool.
I have a friend who has long blonde hair.
I have a friend who likes Irish dancing,
I've never seen her perform,
But I know she is good.
I have a friend who is really pretty,
One day she could be a professional model.
I have a friend who likes singing and dancing,
She thinks she is cool but she's really not.

These are my friends
So ha, ha to you,
I think they're cool,
I don't know about you?

Antonia Giannone (11)
John Warner School

MORNINGS

I wake up. The gleaming sun hits my eyes.
I look out of the window,
The rain drops glisten in the sunlight.
I feel weak,
I stretch my arms,
I move closer to the window
And I open it.
A cold breeze pushes me back!
I'm too cold.
I close the window.
A cold shiver travels down my body.
My feet are freezing,
I cannot stand being cold.
I quickly get back into bed
My head sinks into the pillow.
I slowly close my eyes.
I start to drift off to sleep
And then I have gone.
Zzzzzz.

Alex Burgess (12)
John Warner School

FAIR

As you go into the fair, a sweet smell of candyfloss
Enters the air.
The jingle of money into a hand,
The next thing you're high, high into the sky.
Girls, girls, girls wave your hands.
Lights red, yellow and blue flashing on and off,
You go right, you go left, round and round you go,
You put your hands in the air screaming.

Hook a lucky ball and you're a winner cons the man.
Giggles of laughter as children play.
Round and round on the merry-go-round.
Putting your hand in your pocket to pull out a
Pound, but there's none left, the night is over
Until next time.

Lucy Pickford (12)
John Warner School

SCARY AT NIGHT

I wake up
I see only the pitch black night.
The curtains blow onto my face,
I feel the breeze hitting my chest.
I shiver -
I feel terrified!
I scramble under the bed covers
And clench onto the sheet.
I poke my head out of the bed covers.
I see an enormous shadow!
I start to panic -
The sweat on my body makes my shirt stick to my skin.
I realise it was only a teddy bear.
Sitting comfortably on my blue fluffy carpet.
My heart starts to beat - slower -
I calm down.
I gently place my head back onto the pillow
And fall fast asleep.

Robert Holdstock (11)
John Warner School

THE TREE

The wind is cool
And calm
Swish, swish
Blow, blow,
A breeze upon my cheek
Swish, swish,
Blow, blow,
The wind develops
The tree shakes wildly.
Swish, swish
Blow, blow,
The wind is weakening
Swish, swish,
Blow, blow,
The green leaves in the wind
Swish, swish
Blow, blow,
In the ever dying wind.
Swish, swish
Blow, blow.

Blaise Coull (11)
John Warner School

THE OWL

I swoop down in the middle of the night,
My eyes are shocking yellow,
They glisten in the night light.
Nothing can be heard except for me rustling and hooting,
My ears can hear everything.

My claws are sharp and white,
I can kill anything in sight.
I am hunting now,
A small weak little mouse would be lovely right now,
When I hoot remember, it's me.

Lauren Jones (12)
John Warner School

THE GALA

I stood on the blocks waiting for the gun to go.
Bang! Bang! Bang!
False start.
Oh no!
As I swam back I pulled myself on the blocks,
Again!
Here we are
Bang!
We were off!
I raced as fast as I could.
'Go on Floss'
I heard my mum shout
Wack I hit the rope.
I stopped for a few seconds,
'Go on Floss'
I carried on still as fast.
All of a sudden
I hit the wall.
I stand there wet and ask a very polite man
'What's my time for 1 length please?'
'25.30 seconds,
Well done!'

Lauren Cooper (11)
John Warner School

TRYING TO BE COOL

You're sitting in the rock hard seat
The bar around your waist
The most intense ride
You have ever been on
Spinning around like a rocket
Feeling like you're going to vomit
But you still throw your hands up in the air
Trying to be cool.

You're on the football pitch
Playing your heart out
Trying to get into your local team
Spending all your money on new football kits
That seem to come out monthly
Trying to be cool.

You're sitting in the blue plastic chair
Leaning back on two legs of it
The big angry teacher
Tells you to stop it
You answer her back
And she flips her lid
Her pen goes down on the slip
People laugh
You realise you're not cool
You're just a drip!

Ricky Ellis (12)
John Warner School

THE GORILLA

This is my home
The zoo.
I hate it here being locked up
It's like I have done something wrong.

Here we are again
Zoo's been opened.
Here come all the people
Just standing there waiting
For something to happen.

Well here I go climbing the ropes,
Swing around making people happy,
Here comes dinner at last,
Fruit and vegetables being thrown around.

Zoo being closed,
Time for bed,
We get some more food
Ready for the new day.

Up we get
Ready for the new day
To do it all again.

Claire Taplin (12)
John Warner School

WHAT AN AWFUL WAY TO DIE!

The tired passengers,
Climbed into the trains,
Expecting absolutely nothing,
While the carriages started to move.
As happy as a puppy,
No worries in the world,
The trains went down the track
A big bash!
A big clash!
The roar of the flames were deafening,
The carriages were crushed.
The emergency services rushed in
And saved all the people they could,
While other people lay there,
While other people lay there dead.
What an awful way to die!

Daniel Smith (11)
John Warner School

LIFE OF A MOUSE

The sun rises over the jungle
It wakes me up with a jump,
I hear a roar of an angry lion,
Then the sound of frightened animals.

This goes on all day,
I stay in my hole.
But at night it's my time
Then out I go careful of things.

I see my prey in the grass,
I crawl closer and closer,
Then I catch him off guard
He's my supper for the night.

It's time to go home
That's all the fun for today
The sun will rise tomorrow
And it starts all over again.

Andrew Tweddell (13)
John Warner School

THE LIONESS

I'm a lioness and I'm cruel if you mess with me, you sure are
One hell of a fool,
I run around in my own little world playing nice and
Calm, but then I catch myself, I'm bleeding straight
In the middle of my palm.
I have sharp, sharp, teeth for any little creature that
Steps out of line.
For I'm the leader and I can make room for you in my belly.
'Yes, I caught you now rat' his face is like jelly
His legs are shaking and he's baking in the heat.

'He tastes nice' (apart from his lice in his hair)
Now the chase is on, I hear a mouse but where
Is it? I can smell, oh no I've fell, I've
Lost it now.
I sleep in the bushes, rustling the leaves with flies
Around my head, but then I fall asleep in my
Nice home made bed!

Nicola Richardson (12)
John Warner School

MY RABBIT

When I wake in the morning I look out of my window and see . . .
My little rabbit at the front of his cage.
I go outside to see him, he stands on his back legs.
'I know what you want'
His favourite food - strawberry leaves.
I poke them through the wires,
He quickly takes them from me.
Bite, bite, nibble, nibble.
They're gone in a matter of seconds.
His black eyes look big compared to his tiny body.
He has lots of different coloured hairs
Black, white, grey and brown.
He has a drink, then hides away deep into his hay.
Now I can't even see my rabbit called Harvey.

Katherine Harknett (11)
John Warner School

TIGER, TIGER

Tiger, tiger, come to me,
Run like the ocean pounds the cliffs.
Your colours shining in the sun.
Tiger, tiger come to me.
As you run through the grass you see your prey
But you doubt you will catch it that day.
You run like the wind,
On a stormy night.
There's fire in your eyes tonight.
Slip you do and fall,
There's your prey running away
Tiger, tiger to you I will come!

Lynette Dinmore (12)
John Warner School

I Wish I Wasn't An Evacuee

I went to see my father's grave, he fought in the war
He was being brave,
Now this war is scaring me
I wish I wasn't an evacuee.

The only food we get to eat is rations
They make me weep
My mum has sent me overseas
I wish I wasn't an evacuee.

All I want is to go and see
Is my home where I should be.
I wish my life was filled with glee
I wish I wasn't an evacuee.

Jacob Hoy (12)
John Warner School

A Racist World

It's so cruel this racist world,
Yet some people are only having fun.
Racism crushes the soul inside,
'Nigger' they shouted.
'Move out of the line.'
'Nigger!' they called me, it hurt me inside,
'Where's your family?' they cried,
I thought to myself, I have no family.
They were hung upon our pear tree,
Hung by their necks, with blood red cord.
By a white man, tall and broad,
A racist man from our racist world
Because it's so cruel this racist world.

Frances Williams (13)
John Warner School

THE SUN, THE THUNDER AND THE LIGHTNING

It was a sunny day.
Birds were singing to make the sky fresher and fresher.
Suddenly, it became darker and darker,
Lightning struck and clashed in the dark sky.
Thunder was heading this way,
Rain poured with water,
The birds were twittering with fright,
Everything stopped, the trees were back from
Swaying side to side in the cool breeze.
The sun was coming out from the clouds gleaming with pride,
There was no longer rain pouring from the clouds,
It just turned into a golden, fresh day.

Kylie Savage (11)
John Warner School

FIREWORKS

Fireworks, fireworks,
They go up like rockets
Fireworks, fireworks,
They come down with a bang
Fireworks, fireworks,
Their colours are lovely
Fireworks, fireworks.
They are so loud
Fireworks, fireworks,
There are so many of them
Fireworks, fireworks,
It's hard to choose the best
Fireworks, fireworks,
They are so lovely.

Daniel Lawrence (11)
John Warner School

THE RAT

Crawling around in a small little cage,
Small other rodents who have a terrible rage!
Waiting to die on an uncomfortable mat,
Think of all the cute furry rats.

Tubes and knifes waiting to kill you,
Minute by minute, day by day,
As it gets nearer and you
Know it's your turn,
Your heart beats faster and
Your lungs seem to burn.

When it's your turn
And nobody can help you,
You feel like you've done
Something wrong.
I always know I haven't,
So what am I doing here?
Why am I not in a lovely
Cage with an owner who
Loves me to bits?

I'll tell you why because
Nobody cares,
We were bred,
To be dead!

Laura Cockerell (12)
John Warner School

SILENCE

I hear a sound, where is it from?
From above or down below, what is it?
Don't you hear it?

There it is again,
Tip, tap, tip.
Don't you hear it?
Shall I go to my light switch?
I get out of bed.

I feel the cold air twitch my skin.
I turned on the light, there was nothing there,
I switched the light off.

Can I hear something?

Do you see it?
It's at the dark, cold window, tapping,
It's trying to get in tap, tap, tap it goes again.
I suddenly felt a cold feeling.

Oh no what is it?
It's a ghost!
It's in my room.
Ah . . .

Charlotte Bowey (11)
John Warner School

THE MONKEY

The monkey is a noisy animal,
just like us.
His hands are like ours
His feet are like ours
But does he ever fuss?

The monkey is funky
In fact, very hunky
He will swing with his tail,
if it's blowing a gale.
The monkey is so alike he could
Probably catch a pike.

Stephanie Phillips (12)
John Warner School

RACISM

Years ago when I had to be brave,
my legs and arms chained because I
was a slave,
I didn't ask to be what I am,
my skin the colour black as dirt but
I am still an ordinary man,
shrivelled up in all the smell,
I lived my life in living hell,
screams and cries of bodies in pain,
everyone quiet and going insane,
pitch black was all I could see,
one dead body chained next to me,
months went past I thought
I was going to die,
even men were ready to cry,
I'm still alive to this day
and all I can do is sit and pray,
make sure that no one again
gets treated like this,
everyone's the same and
they should all live in bliss.

Michelle Hackney (13)
John Warner School

RACISM POEM

I hate my life,
I hate school,
people, and everything in it.
From the moment I
walk in the school
gates to the time I
leave, I've cried at
least four times,
People are staring at
me, whispering,
some people aren't
even that polite and
will shout names at me.
Sometimes I just
want to run away,
but what good will that
do, as wherever I go
people will be like it.
I hate my life.
Can you imagine this
happening to you every day?
No, you can't, because
you're white.

Sophie Gosden (13)
John Warner School

NETBALL

Today is the match
I am really scared.
I get in position
And wait patiently for the whistle.
Finally the whistle is blown
It feels like I've been waiting
Waiting
For years
For the whistle.
All the other girls are dodging
And jumping like clumsy fairies.
They pass the ball to me
And I snatch it into my chest.
I swivel around and line up the ball.
My hands are sweaty!
My heart is pounding!
I can feel everyone glaring at me.
I bend my knees, stretch my arms
And jump.
The ball flies from my hands.
It rolls round the top bar.
There is a clap
The ball goes in.
I feel really good inside.
I won, hooray.

Natalie Taylor (11)
John Warner School

GOLDEN TOWN MARKET

Golden town market sweet and fruity
Lots of bananas, apples too.
One by one the jam apples are gone
All that's left is golden run.

A truck load of bananas, apples,
Jam buns, oranges, green limes too,
All the goodness is in you.
All the carrots are orange and ripe,
Like the sun shining down bright,
All the birds flock together with whisky feathers.

Now the birds have gone,
All that's left are cats and dogs.

All the oranges are golden ripe,
As the town prepares for night.
Golden town market,
Sweet and lovely,
Bustling and busy again next Monday.

Michaela Baronowski (11)
John Warner School

THE TIGER

Way deep down in the jungle
A big tiger saw a small mongrel
The tiger chased the dog
The tiger pounced like a thunderbolt
The dog didn't manage to jump the log
He fell over it
The tiger bit the dog - dead.

Mark Hayden Smith (12)
John Warner School

BLACK

Blacks are no good, blacks are no fun
We are hated by everyone.
Being pushed about like slaves,
Having no fun, night and day.
We are not worthy, we are not real.
We're being hung up and killed,
Being stabbed, being hung, being kicked by everyone.
Being thrown into walls and into roads,
No one cares about how we are treated.
As long as it is bad.
Can't walk on pavements we are not worthy.
Cannot go into shops, it's the same
I have lived my life in suffering
But at least I have lived.

David Collins (13)
John Warner School

THE DOLPHIN

The dolphin swims proudly looking for his prey.
After ten minutes he sees a fish. He cannot quite make it out!
He sees blood ahead. As the dolphin turns around, the sharks
Are right there staring straight into his eyes. Crash, the shark bites
Into his blue, long, tail, it starts to bleed straight away.
The dolphin looks back to see if the sharks have gone.
He sees the state of his tail - well what's left of it.
His tail will not stop bleeding, the dolphin
Is getting weaker and weaker. The dolphin goes into the
Seaweed the sharks get tired of chasing him and leave
The dolphin alone for another day.

Mark Cornish (12)
John Warner School

THE PUPPY

I have just been born,
Seeing my first break of dawn.
I smell something nice,
It could be rice or it could be mice.

I am getting colder,
I can't stand up until I get older,
I snuggle up in a little gap,
Going for a little nap.

I have my first bit of meat,
I crawl around with my very small feet,
I hide under the table,
Waiting for my mummy, Mable.

Paul Isham (12)
John Warner School

THE TIGER

I am a big, strong lively bear,
I have a roar like clashing thunder
The thud of my paws flatten the earth as I run
My long glistening tail flows behind me in the sunshine,
My skin is soft and silky like cotton wool from the clouds.

I see prey, deer's on the loose,
My front paws swipe it up,
My powerful teeth are in the deer's skin
And it's gone.
That's been a lovely dinner for the day,
I am the King of the Jungle.

Kirsty Marsh (12)
John Warner School

THE DOG

The dog wakes up and waits,
He waits for his owners to let him out,
Out into the morning sun,
He runs around barking,
Chasing all the cats
And when he has just had quite enough,
He goes indoors and rests.

The dog gets up and walks,
He walks out into the kitchen,
He eats some food,
Then drinks some water,
The owners love him loads.
They treat him like a member of the family,
So the dog is really happy,
He never wants to leave.

Paul Luckett (13)
John Warner School

THE SUNSET BIRD

It comes out in the morning
And goes down at night.
The shades of blue, red, yellow and green
And then the hint of light.
Well.
It isn't the sun going down,
On a warm summer's night.
It was the sunset bird
Saying goodnight.

Jamie Aitchison (12)
John Warner School

The Abandoned Kittens

We are only two days old,
Left on the side of the road,
My brothers are grey,
I am black,
My sister is the colour of the Union Jack.

I wonder where we came from
A yard, farmhouse, or heap
Left in the haystack
Fast asleep.

One day I will be old, just wait and see
And I won't leave my kittens
On the side of the street.

Leighanne Piggott (12)
John Warner School

The Snake

The snake slithering through the
grass, he can see his prey, he
moves closer, he sees the mouse.
The mouse is unaware of the
snake until it is too late.
The mouse is caught,
the snake is full.

The snake slithers back to his
rock were he lays and basks
in the bright white sun and
when it is time, he will strike
again and take another life.

Lewis Richardson (12)
John Warner School

THE MOUSE

I lie in my cage waiting
Waiting for whatever pain I go through next,
Why are they doing this?
The question runs in my head
Why do this to me?

So many questions all unanswered?
Am I next or will I be left
Or will I see others go through too?
Will the white coats set me free
Or will someone come and rescue me
And save me from this torture?

No food, no water,
No one else around
And every now and then
I hear a scream of pain
And ever now and then
This question plays again
Why are they doing this?
Why are they doing this to me?

Siobhan Tomsett (12)
John Warner School

THE BUNNY RABBIT

The little baby bunny rabbit hops about
With his springy step,
Watching for anything to go past.
He is so happy wiggling his
Cotton-bud tail.
Like a ball of fur when he is down.
Then tall as a large flower that
Is fully grown.

His pointy ears are so, so tall,
Listening for any trouble
His button nose is sniffing at a daisy.
He leaps and jumps which you
Might find very crazy.
He chases some green healthy grass,
Then with a jump someone comes
And he runs with a blast
To his beautiful brown and green hutch.

Stacey Crouch (12)
John Warner School

THE LION, KING OF THE JUNGLE

The lion, king of the jungle, very big and tough
Prowls around the jungle looking to kill
Everyone goes all stiff and scared and hides away
One person talks about the king in a bad way
Not knowing he's there standing behind him
He's killed instantly without a second to spare.

But everyone's scared of the king
And nobody cares, he's lonely and old
He has no family, no friends
He's alone at night and day
All the power and all the fame
He'll trade it all for a friend.

Sean Burgess (12)
John Warner School

THE JAGUAR

Sprinting across the plain,
Of grass like racers in lanes,
Oh dear there is a piece of
Glass, it goes into the jaguar.
The jaguar weeps while the
Glass falls out.

The jaguar backs up and
Sprinting across the plains again,
Searching for its prey from
Miles away when it catches
It will make your day.

I the jaguar sees a animal
I the jaguar runs faster than
A car, the animal has no time
To get away.
I the jaguar has caught its
Prey while other jaguars are
Still looking for their prey.

This is my life.

Rikki Woolford (12)
John Warner School

MY CAT JESSY

I have a cat called Jessy
And in the winter, she sits by the fire.
When she plays with her toys,
She is very messy.
She is not like the other cats.
She stays indoors, by the telly.
She sits in my room like a
Plant as still as a flower pot.

When it's time for tea,
She eats a lot.
She is black as coal and
Has eyes that shine
And at night I hear the cats
Outside pine, to be let in.

Lucy Evans (12)
John Warner School

THE CAT

Climbing and climbing up a wall
Chasing and stopping a ball.
Like a flash of lightning up the stairs,
Why do they like sitting on chairs?

They clean themselves here and there
And never leave a bit bare.
They don't like getting wet
But they're still the perfect pet!

Jamie Vella (12)
John Warner School

OUR PET

I don't know how you can do it?
Just sit around all day
And when everyone's asleep
You come out to play!
You put your food in your
Mouth and cart it around in
Your house, then run around in
Your wheel like a little mouse.
You like to eat nuts and seeds,
Apples, carrots and grapes
But best of all you make me
Laugh by all the things you do!
I come home from school
And there you are just waiting
For me to play with you!

Hannah Davis (13)
John Warner School

CRUEL PEOPLE

Racism is a bad thing,
I walk along the street,
and see eyes glaring,
they make me feel like dirt
like litter on the floor,
Sometimes I get things shouted at me,
'Go home you don't belong here.'
When I hear these noises,
I feel like I will cry,
like I will break down,
to the dirty floor where they say I belong.

Liam Finnigan (14)
John Warner School

WHY SUCH HATRED?

His family burning in their own home,
The smell of burnt flesh rushes through the air,
They've done nothing wrong, except have black skin
The father of the family gets his family out,
He puts a stop to the burning of his home.
The whites move in shouting names 'Scum,' 'Dirt,' 'Blackies.'
As the family leave to go and hide,
The whites start beating the father,
Punching, kicking, spitting, swearing.

What has he done to deserve such punishment?
He is a kind and caring family man,
He has no job, through no fault of his own,
He has committed no crime or sins,
The only crime he has committed in the white man's eyes
Is being born with black skin.

Steven Banting (13)
John Warner School

THE JUMPING RABBIT

Wonderful ways to spend a day,
Bright and sunny in the month of May,
Green sparkling frosted grass,
Then hopping around as trees sway,
Thinking of rabbits making their burrows,
Mud getting sprinkled until,
Look!

Louise McIntyre (12)
John Warner School

BILLY

I have got a dog named Billy
Who is always silly,
He is as big as a horse
And his bark is very coarse,
My dad takes him for walks
That are very hilly.

He is six years old,
He is big and bold,
With a black and tan coat,
He sometimes acts the goat.

This is my dog running fast,
Sailing past this is my dog
Billy!

Andrew Kent (12)
John Warner School

RACISM POEM

I am a coloured person,
people in school take the mick,
because of the colour of my skin,
Sometimes I get upset,
Sometimes I just ignore them,
but sometimes it is hard to control my temper.
But there is no point in losing your temper,
they are not worth it.
They are just sad people,
with nothing better to do.
I'm happy with the way I am.

James Forte (14)
John Warner School

POOR LITTLE BLACK BOY

As the whites run away and snigger,
The black man beaten and lying on the floor,
He can see them running from a distance,
Still chanting that horrible name 'Nigger, nigger!'
They always pick on this black man,
No one knows why,
Or what they achieve,
Bullying and beating people with a darker tan,
Why does this always happen to me?
Because they hate me,
Or maybe they just do it for a laugh,
I wish the same would happen to them, then they would see.

Peter Enefer (13)
John Warner School

THE WOMBAT

I live in Australia in the
great down under and think
of myself as a small furry bear.

I think that a drought is
coming and I am really
starting to feel the fear.

I don't know what to do
or if I should ask a
friend but whatever happens
I still feel the same fear.

The drought is here, it has
come, it has killed a lot of
the animals but I am still here.

Steven Smith (12)
John Warner School

THE T-REX

I am the T-Rex King of the Jurassic,
I am big and tall, not at all small.
I have dark scaly skin
Which can camouflage me quite well.
My eyesight is not perfect
If you stop moving, I cannot
See you but if you move
Once inch, I will be chewing you.
Most dinosaurs know which food
Is mine and if they fight back their life will be mine.
Today someone challenged me.
He ended up, dead and food on the floor.
Other dinosaurs know that I am the
King of all dinosaurs,
Respect me I am a T-Rex.

Christopher Reddy (12)
John Warner School

CUTE CAT

Cute and cuddly, curled up like a fluffy ball,
Soft fur, smooth and sleek like a polished school hall,
Purring happily on the porch.
Crash!
Miaow, shrieks the cat,
He bolts upright and tall,
With staring eyes piercing like two balls of fire wild
In the night,
His claws like daggers, take him off out of sight.
Oh! It's only the dustmen that gave him such a fright.

Nadia White (13)
John Warner School

THE SLAVE TRADE

The ship was big, it was long and tall,
As it sailed they sang their song,
The very big galleon,
It waved its flags as it danced away,
But down at the bottom the black people lay.

Tied up together with chains,
The waves were crashing,
Against the boat,
Everyone was screaming,
No wonder, I would be with that smell for 100 days.

Everyone was scared,
Everyone was cold,
Some were distressed,
Some very old,
If it was me, it would end very quickly.

Matthew Ward (13)
John Warner School

FIRE

The fire flickers with colours so bright
like a firework on a starry night
Smell the lovely cosy smell
of the wood burning to charcoal.
Wonderful sounds fill the room
Flicker, whoosh, crickle, crackle
Sometimes the fire is angry
Sometimes the fire is calm
It flickers away
until I'm asleep.

Hannah Softley (12)
Presdales School

THE CHANGING PONDS

Down at the end of the garden,
Is an old pond full of algae,
The pond is cold and dark,
The pondweed is like green skin,
The little algae leaves are like hair,
The leaves resting on the pond look like staring eyes.
Is it a spooky pond girl, or just my imagination?

There will be lots of changes to the pond in the year 2000.
No spooky pond girl, sparkling water falling into the pond,
Fish darting around in the crystal clear water,
Large white waterlilies in full bloom.
Croaking frogs just sitting there like statues.
Brightly coloured butterflies swooping amongst the foliage.
Lots and lots of changes have been made.
At last we have put down our tools
To enjoy the changes that have been put in place.

Charlotte Keens (11)
Presdales School

BEST FRIEND

What is a best friend?
Please tell me!
Is it a person you walk by down the hall
Or a person you say hello to at the pool?
Is it a person you always meet for lunch,
Or is it a person you fight with and punch?
I don't know what a best friend is.
Please tell me.
I've a feeling she's the one sitting next to me!

Rebecca Selcuk (12)
Presdales School

A BUMP IN THE NIGHT

Under my bed is a frightful bump,
A bump in the night that makes me jump.
Is it a monster, a goblin or a vampire who
Lives under the floorboards of my room?

When at night I go to sleep,
I hide under my covers to watch and peep.
When I hear the menacing thud,
I don't turn to jelly, I turn to mud!

I wake at dawn, the grass touched by dew,
I search under my bed for any new clues,
Any new clues I do not find,
All I hope is that my monster is kind.

Laura Williams (12)
Presdales School

SECRETS IT HOLDS!

Sun, shapes,
Different feelings,
Different shapes, the heart-shaped leaves
of the tree holds the key to a mystery,
Spooky, scary,
Cold with shadows twisted twined brambles wrapped around me.

Lost but found,
Tucked away secretly but now known,
Pond not deep but still and green,
Makes you wonder what secrets it holds.

Rebekah Harvey (11)
Presdales School

I'VE GOT SOMETHING TO TELL YOU

Blue is the sea
As blue as you will be
When I tell you the news
Right in front of me
I don't mean to startle
It's got to be said,
I don't want to tell you,
But it's why I've been sent
I don't need the money,
I don't want the job
How can I tell you?
Can I use your bog?

Francesca Foy (12)
Presdales School

THE DARK POND

I went into a garden,
It was dark and spooky,
There was a pond,
That was dark, deep and mysterious.

It looked like a cold sea,
If you looked hard at it, it looked still at the top
But really ripply at the bottom.

It also looked like a city for the creatures,
It had lots of gaps so they could hide,
And there were lots of different colours.

Clare Levitt (11)
Presdales School

SILENCE

Quiet, green are the only ways to describe it.
Birds singing, sun shining
Looks like the tree is bubbling inside
Still pond not a movement around.
Light green, dark green and a few tints
of orange sprinkled around.

Quiet, green are the only ways to describe it
Presdales engraved on an old wooden bench
Sinking into a quiet place.
Light green dark green and a few tints
of orange sprinkled around.

Quiet, green are the only ways to describe it.
An old filing cabinet in a dark deserted corner
Old rusty railings behind all the green trees.
Light green, dark green and a few tints
of orange sprinkled around.

Samantha Whitworth (11)
Presdales School

MY POEM

The garden is cold and lonely
The bench is beginning to rust
The litter is blown around.

Pretty plants are shooting through the stones
Plants are stretching high
Grey tall trees are beginning to grow green leaves
The pond is sparkling where the sun beams on it.

Zoe Cookson (11)
Presdales School

MY POEM

This place seems kind of cold,
It's still and dark,
There's a tall tree in the middle,
Its leaves are like fans.

Its leaves have little splits in them,
They feel so waxy.
I think the tree is called a gingko.
This garden is like a mysterious garden,
It has cobbled steps going up to dead ends.

The steps are crumbling away,
But they are still in good condition.
The pond has no running or moving water,
It's so silent and brittle still.

Sarah Bunyan (11)
Presdales School

SHELLY, SHELLY

Shelly, Shelly was made of jelly,
She was so wobbly,
She fell on her belly.

Shelly, Shelly was made of jelly,
She was so small,
She lived in a welly.

Shelly, Shelly was made of jelly,
She wore no socks,
So her feet were smelly.

Natalie Newman (13)
Presdales School

THE MAGIC GARDEN

T he magic garden is an enclosed little world.
H armony is the main feature with the dividing line of the world.
E ndless sweetness fills the air.

M ist covers the garden like a white blanket keeping it warm.
A ngry maybe, musical, silent yes.
G ardens and their own mind, with the body to go with it.
I solated in its own soul, with green everywhere, it's like sinking
  into a deep sleep.
C old is half the feeling.

G ardens are the missing piece of our puzzle and
  the key to our happiness.
A mbushed by peace and harmony.
R estricted by the long green gates that hold you back.
D angerous is what it looks like but not what it feels like.
E very time I go I feel a *whoosh* of excitement
N ever-ending the mystery I had, but always carrying it with me.

Georgina Duggan (11)
Presdales School

LIFE IS A FLOWER

The breeze blows for me,
The leaves wave for you.
The sun shines for me,
The shadows appear for you.
The moon comes out for me,
The stars glimmer for you.
The flowers open for me,
Life is like a flower for you.

Harriet Ainsworth-Smith (12)
Presdales School

THE LOST GARDEN

I didn't know it was there
It was a secret garden
I went down the broken path
There in the middle was
a very old, grey, tall tree.
It looks like it's been
there for quite a long time.
Then I saw a pond
It was green, thick and shallow.
You look around and it
is very overgrown with lots of
different coloured green leaves.
There was a corner of rubbish
like sticks and an old cupboard
and a lawnmower and
there was an old bench
which creaked when you sat on it.
In the summer the flowers will be out
and it will look pretty and colourful too.

Melissa Tucker (11)
Presdales School

THE POEM OF THE CENTURY

Time is passing so fast,
The end of the century is
approaching at last.

When the celebrations are done,
We won't be around
to see the next one.

Gemma L Hardy (13)
Presdales School

THE GARDEN

The garden so warm,
The garden so cold,
The garden so peaceful,
The garden so old.

Lots of bushes,
Lots of nettles,
Lots of flowers
With pretty petals.

The garden so warm,
The garden so cold,
The garden so peaceful,
The garden so old.

There is a pond,
With lots of weed,
It is a pond
Where no fish feed.

The garden so warm,
The garden so cold,
The garden so peaceful,
The garden so old.

Emma Reed (11)
Presdales School

AUTUMN

The leaves turn golden brown,
And they all fall down.
The conkers come out,
In autumn they're about.

Berries turn ripe
And I fly my kite
The nights are cold
For I am old.

Charlotte McCarthy (12)
Presdales School

WINTER

Here she comes,
Tumbling down the leaf-covered path,
Chasing away autumn,
Winter is in charge now.

The lake turns to ice as her toe touches it,
Her hair controls the wind.
She blows from her blue, frozen lips,
A snow blizzard forms from her icy breath.

Winter wanders around,
Punishing anyone who dares challenge her.
Staring at them, hissing and howling,
She has no soul, she has no life.

The smell of new, crisp air,
Fills the morning sky.
Winter begins to wilt and melt.
She'll be gone soon, she'll be gone.

Winter curls up and cries,
The spring has taken over.
She has no friends, she begins to die and shrivel.
Her heart is frozen.

Caroline Gooch (12)
Presdales School

IN MY MIND

Have you been to a land
Where the sky is pink
And the grass is blue?
Maybe you've seen the people there,
The quivering holograms
Of friends I am with,
I suppose you haven't been there,
You've probably been somewhere else,
You've probably visited your mind,
But I bet you've never visited mine!

Have you been to a land
Where black bamboo
Sway in winds of 2 x 2?
Maybe you've seen the words
Floating like clouds
In puffs of vocabulary,
I'm sure you haven't been there,
I'd be very surprised if you had,
I think I'll stay with my mind,
And you can stay with yours.

Becky Jarvest (12)
Presdales School

OSTRICHES

They are tall and have long necks,
They can't fly,
If they try they crash and die,
Instead of eating from your hand,
They would prefer to stick their heads in the sand.

Jennifer Gilbert (12)
Presdales School

THE BOTHY GARDEN

It's such a lovely little world,
In the spring.
Flowers growing all around you,
Purples, pinks, reds and green,
It's such a lovely little world,
People eating, drinking, talking and laughing,
It's such a lovely little world
The smells are lovely,
Lavender smells all around you.

But when it turns to autumn,
This is not the lovely little world I remember,
The growing flowers are dying
The purples, pinks, reds and greens are turning brown
The people eating, talking, drinking and laughing have gone inside,
The children are now quietly playing in their rooms
The smells are dying,
This is not the lovely little world I remember!

Stephanie Collier (11)
Presdales School

FUTURE THOUGHTS

Gazing ahead,
Monotony or perhaps opportunity.

Leaving behind,
Melancholy or perchance bliss.

The present,
Destitute or possibly secure.

Life . . .

Rosie Aldridge (14)
Presdales School

DINOSAUR

Some ate meat
Some ate plants
Some had scales
Some liked dark
Some hunt others
Some defend
Some kill others
Others pretend
Some of them hide
Some of them show
Some have pride
All of them grow.
Some were huge
Some were small
Some hated each other
But I like them all.

Louise Blanchard (12)
Presdales School

BREAKTIME

Ding, ding, breaktime arrives,
Hundreds of tiny feet come alive.
Crisp packets open, crisps start to fall,
This ones for the birdie, I hear a pupil drawl.
Time begins, so lots of games commence.
Everything was fine, until little Tommy crashed into a fence.
The teacher waddles around, blocking the sound.
Only ten minutes and they are classroom bound!
Ding, ding, ding, right move it into your classrooms
Where the only sound is a teacher that booms.

Olivia Coleman (12)
Presdales School

THE OWL

It sleeps through the day and is awake at night,
Its wings are broad - could give you a fright.
It flies around, searching for prey,
And then it catches something out of the corner of its eye.
A quick, blunt movement amongst the bushes
With its big, bright eyes, it doesn't let it out of its sight.
Then, when all is quiet, it flaps its silent wings
And approaches its creature of aim at an angle,
Flying blissfully through the night sky.
In one movement it opens its sharp beak
And scoops up its prey,
And then returns to its tree until another day.

Emma Reemer (14)
Presdales School

MY FUTURE

In the future
I hope to ski,
To fly, to sail.

In the future
I hope to sing,
To dance, to act.

In the future
I hope to work,
To have friends, to keep my promises.

In the future all these things
I hope to do.

Lucy Hughes (12)
Presdales School

THE FARM ANIMALS

Horses gallop along the beach
with the wind in their tails like a pair of sails.

Cows grazing in the field
munching grass very fast.

Pigs rolling in the mud
like chocolate sauce hot and runny.

Sheep shearing in the barn
to make yards of yarn.

Swans swimming in the pond
like graceful clouds in the sky.

Anna Hunt (12)
Presdales School

A WINTER'S DAY

W ind is howling,
I   ce is forming.
N   ight is advancing,
T   rees are bare.
E   vening is drawing,
R   ain is pouring.
S   now on the ground.

D   ays are short,
A   nd the cold rules supreme,
Y   et people still love a winter's day.

Claire Barker (12)
Presdales School

THE DREADED CAMP

The Germans came during the night,
they gave my family a terrible fright.
We went into the train with a chuck
it was such a tiny, little truck.

We went off to the dreaded camp,
I felt like a little homeless tramp.
I was parted from my father - where will he go?
My tears came along and make me low.

All my belongings were taken away,
it finally came to the end of this day.
I woke up in a tiny room
every face was full of gloom.

As one day dies, here comes another,
I was separated from my poorly mother.
My mother was taken away to be put at rest,
while I had to work, but not like a guest.

I longed for the day for the war to be over,
I need the luck from my four leafed clover.
I really want to go today
I want my belongings that were taken away.

Today the war has finally gone,
everyone started to sing a merry song.
Unfortunately my father has lost his dear wife,
but he was glad that he could live his life.

Hannah Gibbs (13)
Presdales School

TEDDY'S BATHTIME

I put my teddy in the bath,
not realising the aftermath.
He looked so dirty and forlorn,
he'd been my favourite since I was born.
Then on the landing I met Mum,
gosh, her face as she saw what I had done.
I was dragging my teddy by his ears,
moaning and groaning a face full of tears.
My mum was furious, she went mad,
she kept telling me that I was bad.
Dripping wet he looked such a mess,
soggy and misshapen not at his best.
Mum just snatched him to sort him out,
she was cross there was no doubt.
Dad just smiled, then he laughed,
oh, what a day when teddy was bathed.

Nikki Cahill (12)
Presdales School

KATHY TOOK HER DOG FOR A WALK

Kathy took her dog for a walk,
In her hand a lead.
Kathy so small and full of talk
For her mother she was doing a good deed.

It got very late
Still she hadn't returned
Her mother waiting at the gate
Oh what a lesson she had learned.

Teatime came
And still no sign.
Oh what could have happened
To that daughter of mine.

Here comes the dog
Back from his walk
And a tired little girl
With plenty of talk.

Nicola Cockman (13)
Presdales School

RUNNING FREE

She runs through the deep grass,
Her tail flying in the wind.
She knows no boundaries,
She would go on forever.
That feeling of freedom,
How does she feel?
When I see her running wild,
I would love to know that feeling.
She is so beautiful to look at,
Like an angel from heaven.
With that sweet gentle face,
And those deep loving eyes.
Then she is off again,
Pushing the grass away as she runs,
She wouldn't stop for anything.
Lucy, she is a beautiful mare,
With nothing to stop her.

Katherine Knowles (14)
Presdales School

NIRVANA

A moment of triumph,
In a time of despair.

A smile through the tears,
That flow relentlessly down your cheeks.

An incessant stream of understanding,
Until you have no more left to give.

A beautiful laugh,
When things are miserable.

A ray of hope,
When I have nothing left to believe in.

A burst of light,
Breaking the surrounding darkness.

A wave of comfort,
That gives me strength to carry on.

A persistent feeling of joy,
Though everything around me should cause me sorrow.

A reason for living,
When I was certain I would have to give up.

That's what your love is to me.

Victoria Mann (14)
Presdales School

A BALLAD OF FRIENDS

There's Monica and Joey
Rachel, Chandler, Ross,
There's Phoebe with her triplets
And Rachel's boyfriend Josh.

Don't forget the animals
and the ugly naked guy.
Our friends peer through their window
pretending not to spy!

Monica and Ross are siblings and
wept when their Nan died.
But it wasn't as bad as Phoebe
who's mum committed suicide!

She thought her mum came back
as a cute and cuddly cat.
She sings away her problems
Although her singing's flat!

The boys are in the titchy flat,
along with Duck and Chick.
They've got the swinging leather chairs
that open at a flick!

The girls, they live a luxury life
with a full colour TV.
So the boys come over all the time
To have a laugh with Phoebe.

So that's the group of friends
with not much luck in love.
They can't live without each other
these friends fit like a glove!

Debi Samuels (13)
Presdales School

THE FAIRY IN MY GARDEN

There's a fairy in my garden,
Who lives by the pond,
She sits upon a rock,
And watches everyone.

She has a pair of wings,
And long golden hair,
She wears a flower dress,
And always looks her best.

I went down the garden,
Just the other day,
And she was laid upon a rock,
Not in her normal way.

I gently picked her up,
And laid her on my hand,
No life was in her body,
I felt very sad.

Jill Kittle (12)
Presdales School

COLOURS

A black and white world
With a black and white lane
A black and white house
The colour is so faint.

The streets are dark
There are no trees
No parks, or flowers
Also no bees
Where is the colour, no one can see.

The day slowly faded
Still just black and white
But the new day rose
And the sunset came.

The darkness has faded
And all colour was seen.

Amy Davis (12)
Presdales School

DON'T LEAVE ME

How could you leave me like this?
In a state of turmoil,
Not knowing.

How could you leave me in the lurch?
Too frightened to confront you,
Just tell me.

How could you leave me standing by?
I don't understand your games,
What's your point?

How could you leave me looking like a fool?
I don't find it amusing,
I need to know.

How could you leave me when I needed you?
Give me a reason,
I must be told.

Why have you left me?
Why haven't you spoken to me?
Please don't leave me.

Emily Hanson (14)
Presdales School

MY MENTAL CAT

My cat is gentle,
Yet, can go mental:
He sits on the floor,
Then jumps up a tree,
Runs into my door,
Mental - do you agree?

My cat is sentimental,
Yet, can go mental:
He lays on the mail,
Then chases his tail.
Cuddles me close
To protect him from his enemies
I suppose!

My cat is mental - don't you see.
He's mental - do you agree?

Lorna Middlewood (12)
Presdales School

PLUM FAIRY

She dances round the frosty webs,
In search of a quiet place,
She finds a plant soft and still,
Then her melting finger touches the branch,
And there grows a small round plum,
Juicy and purple, they grow like mushrooms,
Her fairy friends dance with her,
As they make the frosty winter into warm spring.

Ffion Cummins (12)
Presdales School

SLEEPING BEAUTY

A child was born in a kingdom, and blessed that very day
by three magical little fairies, who danced the night away.

A wicked witch then came, blessing not her game,
a curse she put upon the child, succeeding in her aim.

Away the child was taken, to a pretty little house,
with the three magical little fairies and a tiny weenie mouse.

There she stayed for sixteen years, to the palace she then returned
the king was sure for her safety, after all the spinning wheels burned.

But as she arrived at the palace, she saw a bold, bright light,
she followed it round the castle, into the dreamy night.

Then she came to a small square room, where sat a spinning wheel
touch me, touch me, touch me, this was the wicked witches deal.

To the ground the princess fell, all to be heard was the wicked witch's
laughter, she left her lying on the floor and in came the fairies after.

Upon the bed she lay, whilst the kingdom in a sleep,
the prince was fighting for their love, hoping it would keep.

The prince had won, all was well,
the princess was safe and the witch in hell.

Another fairytale ended, just the way it should,
everything turned out right, I always knew it would.

Tara Fowler (13)
Presdales School

HIMSELF

Do you want to be here?
Does it make you smile?
Do your eyes light up
Or do they mock?
When you talk to me
What do you feel?
The opposite of what you are saying
Or an unlimited version of it?
If the world is not black and white
How much of it makes you a bad person?
Do you get my drift
Or are you tactless
Like everyone else?
If so,
What makes me,
Wonder about you so *much*?

Viola Mullen (14)
Presdales School

BONFIRE NIGHT

Screaming fireworks
Flying so high.
Fountains of colour
Illuminate the sky.

Bonfire blazing
Burns the sorry man.
Startled as I looked up
A firework went bang!

Children making patterns
With sparklers in the air.
Rain begins to fall
But nobody seems to care.

Catherine wheels are spinning,
Whizzing rockets fly.
Now the show is over,
It's time to say goodbye.

Katherine Hall (12)
Presdales School

THE LAST ROAD

Chasing through the trees,
Racing through the breeze,
I ride.
Winding through the light,
Blinding to my sight,
I glide.
Speeding down the lane,
Needing to feel pain,
I dash.
Fleeing from the fear,
Seeing the car near,
I crash.
Lightning through the rain,
Whitening with the pain,
I cry.
Wanting to live no more,
Wanting to close the door,
I die.

Joanna Rose (14)
Presdales School

Dan, He's The Man!

Dan, Dan, he's the man,
He eats, sleeps and drives in his van,
He doesn't care if he's really smelly,
He picks his nose and scratches his belly.

He cleans his teeth with a toilet brush, yuk!
There is no water, so no baths! That's just his luck,
I feel sorry for him, other kids call him names,
They laughed at him, when his van went up in flames!

It's not his fault that he's really smelly,
It's not his fault he scratches his belly,
And it's not his fault he washes his clothes in a frying pan!
Dan, he is definitely the man.

Alexa King (12)
Presdales School

A Fairy's Tale

I float amongst the autumn leaves,
And fly around the willow trees.
I live in the river with ducks and fishes,
And grant you all your cherished wishes.

I sit in the tulips every day,
And when it is winter I dream again,
Of all the children in their sleep,
And all the animals you do keep.

I am the fairy of the lake,
You will see me when you're not awake,
I am the fairy in your dreams,
Maybe I am, or so it seems.

Natasha Peedle (11)
Presdales School

GUILT

I walked away
I left you standing there
For a second I was relieved
For *one second* I was happy
And *I'm sorry*
It only takes a second
To ruin a lifetime
And *I'm sorry*
It only takes *one* thought
To break a bond
And *I'm sorry*
And I know that when you picture me
I stand alone
Surrounded by dark
And *I'm sorry*
And I know that if you coloured me in
The only colours you could use, would be
Black and white and grey
And *I'm sorry*
And I know
I know that when you think of me
It is the only time you are unhappy
And *I'm sorry*
I walked away
I left you standing there
And *I'm sorry*
I'm sorry.

Kristiania Crilly (14)
Presdales School

TROUBLED SOUL

The girl stood with curiosity,
Looking around,
She knew it was all the same,
The feelings, the thoughts, the words.
She glared with great despair
about the misfortunes of life.

The human race,
What a classic case of indifference.
People with their high expectations,
Wanted more each day,
While confusion entered her life day by day.

Looking back, she realised how difficulties invaded her mind,
Blocking her way forward.
But she passed through somehow,
Forgetting there was still more to do,
Still more things to fit together.

Without even a thought or wonder people continued to judge.
She thought she knew what was right,
But more questions conquered her mind.

She looked far beyond what the eyes usually see
to realise the existence she claimed,
Was far less than seemed
as there's still so much to learn.

She observed things through different perspectives
and one day she knew,
There will be no more regrets, no more sorrow, no more
                                      misunderstanding,
The ignorant minds about the way we are supposed to be will vanish.

People with their feelings, thoughts and words,
Might one day change
To realise life is not all it seems.
To know there is always more to understand
And always more challenges to face.

Nisha Samani (14)
Presdales School

HOW UGLY I AM NOW!

How ugly I am now!

It seems that a lifetime ago,
I could walk down the street,
With my skirt in my knickers,
And I wouldn't care!
No one would care!

My eyebrows are definitely thicker,
My hair won't stay put,
My skin is so spotty,
And now I see it!
Everyone sees it!

Long legs! (Trousers too short!)
Big bum! (Skirts are too taut!)
Buying clothes? Nothing fits right!
Could I have changed so much over night?

I used to be young and couldn't care less,
Ne'er looked in a mirror I have to confess,
Had I looked, would I see what I now see?
That very same image, now important to me?

Marika Opara (15)
Presdales School

YOU TOOK AWAY MY WINGS

You took away my wings,
And left, to take your place.
A chain around my neck,
It makes the fall much worse,
For the longer I fall the tighter it gets.
With time I lose all feeling,
You never had a reason to distrust me,
After all that was said.
So I sit in silent protest,
My cause?
A fight you know not of.
I will fight my grisly battle,
In my room and in my silence.
And you, the enemy,
Will never know.

Victoria Smith (14)
Presdales School

ODE TO MY LITTLE ONE

The future belongs to you little one,
I pray for it to be brighter than mine was,
And for it to give you the opportunities
That I never had.

The world is yours to explore little one,
I hope that you discover places
That I would never dream of,
But still have somewhere to call 'home'.

The good times are yours to be enjoyed little one,
I wish for you to have more happy memories than I have,
But for you to be independent,
And able to support yourself.

The future belongs to you little one,
I pray for it to be brighter than mine,
But if it isn't,
I'll always be here for you.

Julia Ryan (14)
Presdales School

LOMBAFLOB

Enwrapped in an incessant wrath,
Just as it does cross my shadowed path.
Panic-stricken I fight to flee,
Life and death lies between the beast and me.

Compelled in a hypnotic trance,
Upon me the Lombaflob does advance.
Eyes blazing, despite the darkness of night,
And phantom lips chanting, improving my fright.

Nearer he comes, his breath I can feel,
Is there hope left, is my nightmare real?
Intense is the moment, drenched in cold sweat,
Our skin may have touched, but our eyes have not met.

I breathe my last breath, my final sigh heaved,
But the following moment, my horrors are relieved.
An ear-piercing yell erupts from the chants,
And to continue a thud, and a chance.

Stephanie Anne Bryan (11)
Presdales School

I WISH...

Sometimes I wish I was invisible,
Incapable of saying these cruel words,
The ones I can never take back.
Sometimes I wish I was invisible,
Unable to see myself when I play back the
humiliating scores in my head.
Sometimes I wish I was invisible,
So they couldn't be aware of me,
Aware of me to stare at me,
Stare at me to scare me.
Sometimes I wish I was invisible,
So you couldn't see me crying,
Crying through your taunting,
Crying because I'm not invisible.

Jennifer Wooden (15)
Presdales School

SAILING BOATS

Children come, come and play,
Boys and girls and adults too.
Joining hands and having fun,
They sail their boats in the sun.

Blue, green and red ones too,
Dots and stripes and paint spots too.
They glide along the wavy water,
The children take their shoes to go and have a paddle.

Then Mum calls, time to go,
They say goodbye to their fellow friends.
Their boats too.
Bye, bye.

Holly Tetlow (12)
Presdales School

THE CREATURE OF THE DARK

An alien like vision,
With a head thrice as large as mine,
And eyes like staring saucers,
And no nose to be seen.

A metallic mouth,
With grinning, sharp teeth,
There the face finishes,
With no chin to be seen.

A neck like a broomstick,
Widening at the bottom,
A shining, narrow forehead,
And no hair to be seen.

A bodiless phantom,
A ghostly, colourless thing,
A screaming, terrifying monster,
Like nothing ever seen before.

Joanna Franklin (12)
Presdales School

CHILDREN

Children come and go,
Happily playing in the garden.
In their tree houses up high,
Laying in the sun.
Dreaming about sweet things,
Running through the bushes.
Enjoying the scene,
Night falls and they all disappear.

Sarah O'Leary (12)
Presdales School

MYSTERIOUS WORLD

Steam drifts upwards,
Off a burning lake,
Palms tall and intimidating,
A paradise or heaven.
I wonder if it's inhabited
Probably not,
But it must be.
Blue skies,
And sunshine,
A bubbling lake,
Woods,
I turn and see a feast of food,
My friends all around,
Calling me
As I run,
It turns back into pollution and poverty,
Back as usual, again.

Emma Martin (11)
Presdales School

CHILDREN

Children screaming,
Having lots of fun
In the park
With lots of mums.

Swings so high
They nearly reach the sky.
Roly-polys on the ground,
All the world is spinning round.

Eating lollies
Is oh so much fun,
Then there's the best bit
'Bubblegum'.

Going home
Is oh so boring
But then we have got
Tomorrow morning.

Katie Sampford (12)
Presdales School

THE HOUND FROM HELL

There stands the dog with short, spiky hair,
Its red evil eyes glare,
Its ears shoot back straight as a warning,
It throws its head back and barks till morning.

It stands its feet strongly to the ground,
This is a warning from the beastly hound.

The slimy, twirling, tangled vipers is up its back,
Spitting out poison, they're grey as the night.

The main evil snake shoots out as a tail,
Whirling and twirling, red devil eyes, no need for a trail.

Face crinkled up, in hate and in anger,
I staggered back, a chill down my spine.

Wanting to run from Theseus the hound from *hell,*
Too scared to move, a lump in my throat.

Run! I say run! Or I'll forever be done.

Alexandra Burns (11)
Presdales School

THE CIRCUS

Honk, honk!
Bonk, bonk!
Here comes the clown's car.

The clowns are round,
Bold and found
In the circus.

With their red noses
They start to pose,
Throwing custard pies!

If you want to have some fun
Come along and see . . .

Jugglers, acrobats and fire-eaters too,
They put on their act just for you.

Hollie Davis (12)
Presdales School

WEIRD WORLD!

Cars whizzing through the air
People driving without a care.
Metallic robots glinting in the sun
People in silver clothes - oh what fun!
People living in space.
Oh! What a weird human race!
We all have flying suits,
And very odd bouncing boots.
Robots being taught to sing,
Isn't the future a funny thing?

Kelly Shimmin (13)
Presdales School

A NEW MILLENNIUM

The new millennium
Is nearly here,
What will happen
This new year?

Will we have
Another world war?
Will thousands of people
Keep breaking the law?

Will we live
In peace and harmony?
Will thousands of people
Still be hungry?

Will the rainforest
Be destroyed?
Will thousands of
People still be unemployed?

Will people still
Live without a home?
What will happen
To the Millennium Dome?

For this new millennium
We should make a resolution,
For the world to try
And find solutions.

Alexandra Walker (14)
Presdales School

MY FIRST LITTLE POEM

My first little blink,
My first little cry,
My first little giggle,
My first little sigh.

My first little step,
My first little walk,
My first little word,
My first little talk.

My first little ride,
My first little bike,
My first little holiday,
My first little hike.

My first little job,
My first little pound,
My first little joy in life,
That I have found.

My first little son,
His first little cry,
His first little giggle,
His first little sigh.

Talitha Proud (12)
Presdales School

CAN I HAVE A LOOK?

Can I have a look?
I want a look!
I want a look now!
Can I have a look?
I want a look!
I'm asking nicely please!

Do you like me,
Are you sure?
If you liked me you'd let me see!
You don't like me!
Why?
Please tell me!
I've done nothing wrong!
What have I done to you and anyone?

Katie Golding (12)
Presdales School

HUNGRY HOUND

There was a poor dog,
who was left all alone.
So he ordered a pizza,
by telephone.
The delivery man shared it with him,
for he was lonely.
And the pizza he ordered,
was pepperboni.
When the delivery man had gone,
he still wanted more food,
So he strolled down the High Street,
he really was shrewd.
He found a Chinese restaurant,
and ordered Chow Mein.
And as soon as he finished,
it started to rain.
He ran back home,
so he would not be found out.
And no one ever knew,
he had been out and about.

Martha Dellar (13)
Presdales School

STARS

Every time you look
at the stars,
the brightest one
will be me.
Watching you
from afar
because my love
is eternal as a star.
Forever I will be by
your side, no matter
what I'll be there, like
your guardian angel constant
and true for you.
No matter where
I am I will
travel far and wide
for you.
I will bring you the moon,
I will cross the sea to
be by your side.
I will be there.

Robyn McFayden (12)
Presdales School

THE MERMAID

The colourful orange sun rose above the horizon,
It shone down on a tiny figure curled up on a jagged rock.

The sun shone and brightened up her silvery green scales,
They gleamed like diamonds.

Her hair was lengthy and as thick as a forest,
She gently combed her golden tresses while softly humming to herself.

Her porcelain-like skin was just like a china doll's
And her eyes were as blue as the ocean.

Hannah Spearpoint (11)
Presdales School

RECOVERY

I've never felt as frightened as I do right now,
Never wanted anything more,
For you to recover is all I ask,
I pray for your return.
Your smiling face, your way with words,
The way you made me laugh,
Recover, please, I beg of you,
Come home, make a fresh start.

You never should have left that night.
The road was wet and it was dark,
That argument is my deepest regret,
I hated having to shout.
But you wouldn't listen, even then,
Stubborn as you always were,
You wanted your own way,
You always did,
Look where its got you now.

But we'll put it all behind us,
Make changes if you like,
My son, I love you more than I can say,
And I beg you to be alright.

Eleanor Clark (14)
Presdales School

PAGES OF HISTORY

As we turn the pages of time,
We await for a new beginning,
Fear, anger, hate and suffering will be no more,
War, hunger, greed and crime will be faded
                              memories in the pages of history,
As we write history today,
Our future lies unwritten,
To rewrite these pages would mean the hope of a better life.
Who knows what the future will reveal to us,
We will never know until we see what will be
                              written in the future book of history.

Fiona Man (14)
Presdales School

FAIRIES

The fairies that live in the bushes and trees
Fly around in the wind and the breeze,
They are purple and pink with silver wings,
The oldest one dances and sings.
Some of them are only five centimetres tall,
Compared to us that is very small.
They love flying around
And landing on the ground.
When they see danger coming
Or they hear the bumblebees humming,
They run back to their holes away from danger
Because to them, everyone is a dangerous stranger.

Lucy Anderson (11)
Presdales School

UNICORN MAGIC

I was walking out in the cool night breeze
When suddenly I noticed something moving in the shadows,
I walked closer to the mighty beast,
And saw it glinting in the moonlight
What is this gorgeous animal?
I can't see it clearly enough,
Then finally it comes forward,
And I see, at last, the beauty of the Unicorn.

Beneath the horn of the steed
I see a deep green emerald.
I try to touch the amazing beast,
Although he moves back away to the shadows.

The magnificent Unicorn
Mystery of the world.
I have seen it all!
I am the lucky one
As the Unicorn is a secret well kept!

Stephanie Mann (11)
Presdales School

BADGERS

Just looking, just smelling, just listening,
The badgers are so cautious.
Just sniffing, just walking, just talking,
The badgers are so careful.
Just clean, just hungry, just snorting,
The badgers scavenging for food.
Just squinting, just moving, just hurrying,
The badgers don't want to be seen.

Charlotte Stevens (11)
Presdales School

MY BEST FRIEND

I saw this happening right before me,
He would put on a brave face to the outside world,
But I knew there was something wrong,
He confided in me,
From that day onwards everything changed,
I grew older,
Soon everyone knew after his many treatments,
People treated him differently,
His whole attitude towards life changed,
He was suddenly so lively and outgoing,
However, I saw his low points,
Slowly, I saw this disease eating away at him,
I saw the tears in his eyes,
I saw his pain and sickness,
I saw him die.

Sonal Mistry (15)
Presdales School

HOW DO YOU SEE IT?

The future; we all see it differently.
Will it come peacefully?
Will it come destructively?
Will it be frightening?
Will it be exciting?
Will there be new technology
Or will things stay as they ought to be?
The millennium has come;
How do you see it?

Kate Carson (15)
Presdales School

THE WORLD I LIVE IN

You were born
A picture of innocence,
Not knowing what would happen in life,
What you would do,
But you did it anyway.

You were a young woman,
Naive and carefree,
Smoking sixty a day
And ignored the advice
But you did it anyway.

You were middle-aged,
A responsible person.
You drove your car
When you could have walked
But you did it anyway.

You died at sixty,
Too young for it to happen.
Perhaps all the booze
Took its toll in the end,
Too late now, anyway.

But now I live in this place
That you left far behind.
It's dirty,
Polluted
And you did nothing to stop it.

Charlotte Forbes (14)
Presdales School

THE FAIRY

She flew by, fast and light.
It was dark, in the middle of the night.
Her delicate wings fluttered to and fro,
And gave off a faint friendly glow.
Around her shoulders fell long, brown hair
Even if you tried not to - you couldn't help but stare.
On her head she wore a fluffy, blue hat,
She had a tiny blue dress on which I saw when she sat.
On a branch at the top of the tallest tree,
A squirrel would find hard to climb, let alone me!
She was no taller than a safety pin
I noticed she was quiet and never made a din.
In her hand she held a glittery wand,
Which looked magical in her reflection when she flew
over a pond.
Suddenly she flew off into the night,
Maybe I'll see her again, you never know, I might!

Chloe Taylor (11)
Presdales School

FASHION

T-shirts, polo shirts, the roll-neck make,
Tight shirts, baggy shirts, designer and fake.

Short skirts, long skirts, loose, tight fit,
Pleated skirts, A-line skirts, the skirts with slits.

Pedal-pushers, jeans, hipsters or shorts,
Trousers under skirts or tracksuits for sports.

Wool coats, fur coats, denim and leather,
Anoraks, puffa jackets or coats for all weathers.

Bright colours, dull colours, subtle or bold,
Blue colours, red colours, silver and gold.

Jewellery and make-up in all kinds of makes,
Fashion statements and breakthroughs
And fashion mistakes.

Eva Wilhelm (14)
Presdales School

ASA

She is as black as the night
And she is soft and cuddly.
In the night she might give you
A fright
But she is kind and like a
Puppy.

Her nose is black, her feet are black
And her ears are black too
Her best friend was a cat called
Smudge
And he was black and white too.

We used to take her to a river
At least once a day
She would wait for a command
Even when she wanted to play
To me she is the best dog in
The world.

Joanna Hart (11)
Presdales School

The Mythical Python

They called it the almighty python,
To be seen when skies were clear.
Although brave knights called it a legend,
Of it the townies were afeared.

That night the skies were starry,
And the moon was out.
You could hear the flapping of wings,
But was it just the bats about?

A crowd soon was formed,
As if frozen, stood in fright.
Their nightmares had become reality,
Before them stood the horrific sight.

It displayed its bloodstained teeth,
It's head held high and proud.
Then roared a mighty roar,
To scare away the crowd.

It flapped its wings frantically,
And prepared to take flight,
Then rose into the air,
And disappeared into the night.

Amy Millard (11)
Presdales School

As A Child

When you are young protection is vital,
People hold your hand at every step.
And as you grow the grip is loosened,
Freedom and independence are longed for.
Sometimes they are granted, and often unwisely,
But people are always there to pick up the pieces.

And soon, all too quickly, adulthood begins,
The sheltered life is shattered and the world enlarges.
A new life begins with all its joys and hazards,
But there are no people standing by to help.
They are far away and missing the old life.
This is the freedom longed for, you are ready to live it,
You are no longer a vulnerable child.

Eleanor Gower (15)
Presdales School

THE FAIR

Bright red, green, orange and yellow lights,
Fairground music bursts through the night.

The whirling, curling of the rides
The smell of grease they try to hide.

The sticky taste of candyfloss
To be without would be a loss.

The Hoopla, the Coconut, such great games
Even the man who can eat flames.

The Ferris Wheel goes round and round
While others like to stay on the ground.

The rides pick up, going faster and faster.
Below you can hear screams of laughter.

Those rides can be really bad for you
They make you feel sick with flu.

The fairground comes but once a year,
But still you remember it crystal clear.

Jessica Stacey (13)
Presdales School

HOMELESS IN A STATION

As I walk by on my way to work
I see a woman with a tattered skirt.
Her face is black
And her hair is wild,
In her arms is a screaming child
With a box as a cot
And no rattle or toys.
The mother sings to her baby boy
A soft lullaby to send baby to sleep,
The voice of an angel so tender and sweet.
The child is silent and cries no more,
His mother lies down on her bed on the floor.
I think of my flat with hot water and heat,
My warm cosy bed, I've plenty to eat.
In my bag a twenty pound note,
She needs it more than I need a new coat.
I bend slowly to give her the twenty,
She seems to be sleeping
So I shake her gently.
I place the money into her thin cold hand,
She takes the money but still looks sad.
I get up quickly and turn to walk off,
I hear a weak voice and then a cough.
As I look back
She starts to speak,
'Ta for the money
I ain't eaten all week.'
I smile at her and walk to my train,
Then I hear the baby cry again.
As I sit down I think of the lady,
The poor homeless lady
With her baby.

Victoria Sneddon (14)
Presdales School

THE BEST GRANDAD IN THE WORLD
(Dedicated to my great grandad, George Kames Basham)

My grandad is the best in the world,
His hair so soft you can cuddle it and never let go,
His teeth so white they were like snow,
Of course they were false.

I used to sit and cuddle him tight,
I'd never let go for eternity and beyond.
We had a very special bond,
That we will keep forever and ever.

He owned a sweet shop,
Then on to a betting shop.
His shops (I'm told)
Were rather special.

He enjoyed his football very much,
Tottenham Hotspurs he loved.
He'd go to every home game,
With my Nanny and Brian, a friend.

My grandad is the best in the world,
His hair so soft you can cuddle it and never let go.
His teeth so white they were like snow,
Of course they were false.

Francesca Rose (13)
Presdales School

BEWARE OF SCHOOL

Everyday we walk into school
With its blood-red pool.
Silently standing in an orderly line,
Waiting to sign.

The doors are closed for the rest of the day,
We are made to pay
For all our crimes,
Like losing a dime.

Maths, Science, English, French,
We all sit on an old creaky bench,
At ten to four the doors open
And we are free.

We're young and supposed to have fun
But instead we're hard done.
We should be free
Like a fuzzy bumblebee.

Harriet Aldridge (11)
Presdales School

WHAT AM I?

Silent, swift, gliding through the skies,
Scaly wings, beady eyes,
Small, furry body hanging upside down,
This creature never falls to the ground,
Fruit is what this thing eats,
In the day it's asleep,
What is this creature, have you guessed?
This little thing is a: *bat!*

Louise Underhill (11)
Presdales School

THE PLATYPUS

The platypus is an amazing thing,
it resembles a garden mole,
Though it has a duck bill and is covered
in hair
it lives in a deep, dark hole.

It swims in rivers, ponds and lakes,
in some parts of Australia.
Laying its eggs in nests quite full
of its paraphernalia.

Not many people know of it.
If they did it would cause a fuss.
It's the happy, snappy, flappy, platy,
Duck-billed platypus!

Katherine Bexfield (13)
Presdales School

GRIFFIN

Eagle and lion with wings and tail
Flying up high feathers quite pale.
With claws and beak to catch prey
It may be still and might run away.
If you're too big for this mythical creature
Your flesh is probably his favourite feature.
This animal is really quite rare, his gold feathers
and tail and hair.
I am talking about a Griffin the most deadly
creature I know
I would insist to not put him on show.

Danielle Coletta
Presdales School

THE TINY WOOD PEOPLE

The cold, misty moon gave a dim light
to the tiny wood people hiding in trees.
They looked down on the damp ground,
    a thick carpet of dark leaves.

The boughs swung low in the whimpering wind,
casting deep, cursing shadows on the forest bed.
While the tiny wood people hiding in their trees
    swayed to and fro in the lightening breeze.

The scent of dawn turned the white moon foggy,
    and all traces of night were lost.
    The spider webs glistened with dew,
and the tall, green grass was frozen with frost.

The tiny wood people jumped from their hides,
    and thinned out in a long line.
The leader crept quietly forward making no noise,
and they entered a clearing where a large mound was poised.

The mound was lit and the fiery, flames flickered,
    letting ashes float up then fall to the ground.
    Two tiny wood people held out their drums,
and with two wooden sticks they started to pound.

The tiny wood people danced out the dawn,
and the tiny wood people danced out the dusk.

The tiny wood people were quiet once more,
    and the fire had long died out.
The tiny wood people again hid in their trees,
the leader would hush them, 'Good night!' he would shout.

The cold, misty moon gave a dim light
to the tiny wood people hiding in trees.
They looked down on the damp ground,
a thick carpet of dark leaves.

Victoria Lawton (11)
Presdales School

CREAM AND STRAWBERRY CAKE

There in the kitchen
stood a cake, all yummy.
At the same time I was thinking
it will soon be in my tummy.
Sponge cream and strawberries all mixed up.
I would have had mulberries but they're really yuk!
I'm getting ready to unlock my jaw
to have yummy cake and then more and more.
I'll get the knife out of the drawer,
if not I'll use my paw.
I crept over just going to have a nibble,
but then Mum came and put it in the middle
of the table in the dining room and when I went
over there, I saw doom!
The cake was gone
Not even a crumb was left
It was all gone.

Danielle Williams (11)
Presdales School

THE MERMAID

On the rocks sat the mermaid
The one with the long shiny hair.
She was as fat as a nut,
But she swam like a duck.
Her legs pointed up but her toes pointed down.
Everyone else thought she looked like a clown.
She had fins like a hook,
And glared just like soot.
You've never seen anything quite like her foot.
I better not give too much away,
Apart from the fact that her name is Fay!

Sarah Duxon (11)
Presdales School

MEDUSA

The name of Medusa
Chilled all to the bone.
If you looked in her eyes
You'd be turned into stone.

She was a mythical creature
Who lived deep in her lair.
She had bright red eyes
And snakes for her hair.

A hero called Perseus
Said 'I'll cut off her head!'
With one blow of his sword,
And Medusa lay dead.

Danielle Laura Keys (11)
Presdales School

WHERE WILL I BE IN THE FUTURE?

I'm going off to live in space,
On Saturn, Jupiter or Mars.
Oh what an exciting journey
Off to see the stars.

Will I be driving a car,
or will my mum be driving me?
Will I be floating around?
I'll just have to wait and see!

Will I be living on a space-station?
Will I grow an extra foot tall?
Will I ever visit the moon,
or travel through the asteroid wall?

What will I have to eat?
What will I have to drink?
Will I have an alien encounter,
and what will it really think?

Perhaps I'll travel the world,
or maybe I'll stay at home.
I may not even go up into space.
But just stay home alone.

Susie O'Hara (13)
Presdales School

ROBOTIC CAT

Will they eat, will they sleep?
Will they purr, take the heat?
Will they be happy, will they be sad?
Will they be good, or will they be bad?

Will they like light, or will they like dark?
Will they eat dog, or will they eat shark?
Will they like bat, will they like frog?
Will they like mice, and will they like hog?

Will they bark, will they whinge?
Will they shriek, and make you cringe?
Will they move, or will they stay still?
Will they be healthy, or will they be ill?

Will they be evil, or will they be nice?
Will they catch rats, or will they catch mice?
Will they be thin, or will they be fat?
Nobody knows for the robotic cat.

Sarah Vince (13)
Presdales School

THE PHOENIX

In barren heat beneath the shining sun,
Watched by the sphinx with stony glare,
The glowing embers shimmer on the sand,
As the golden phoenix rises in the air.

The metallic gold creature soars upward,
His wings stretching out as he flies,
Of gold and of saffron, of crimson,
Below him the vast desert lies.

The sun rises and sets over Egypt
For five hundred years, day and night.
The flowing Nile glistens eternal,
The pyramids witness the sight.

The fabulous creature is ageing,
He senses his fate is at hand,
As the sun sets over the desert,
The flames draw him back to the sand.

Camilla Harris (11)
Presdales School

MEMORIES

The gentle sound of the teacher's voice.
She runs through the list on the register,
Eager smiles look on admiringly,
Sitting cross-legged on the itchy carpet,
Dazzling colours shine off the crowded walls,
The warm sun smiles as it beams through the window.

Baggy art overalls streaked in runny paint,
Practising the alphabet and counting one to ten,
The class hamster curled up in her cotton-wool bed.

Playtime couldn't be more happy,
The sound of laughter carried all over the playground,
The fresh, bright colours on the climbing frame,
Children jumping, skipping and twirling.

Young mothers arrive to collect their children,
Who wave and shout goodbye,
Eager and excited,
For there will be a whole new day tomorrow.

Abby Cottrell (13)
Presdales School

TIPTOEING AWAY

T he noise is lost when he is there
I open the door and he's in my chair
P iles of dust are on his floor
T o see him is so much more
O nce again he's in my house
E ven now he watches my mouse
I n the water I see him now
N arrow-minded he makes no vow
G ently he tiptoes to your bed

A nd snatches the life inside your head
W hen morning comes
A nd the sun is high
Y ou are him and meant to die!

Rachael Holm (12)
Presdales School

MY FUTURE

I hope my future will be bright
like a shining star at night.
My wish for everyone will be
for them to be happy.
Will there be flying cars
and people living in and on Mars?
Will we reach the year 2001
or will there be no more fun?
In the future what will I be?
I'll just have to wait and see!

Elizabeth Smyth (13)
Presdales School

THE PARROT SONG

People think that I talk too much
and what a weird pet,
but I think I'm the best in the world,
because I chatter, chatter, chatter.

I miss being out in the wild,
with the cuckoo, pigeon and friends,
but eating and sleeping all day,
has got to be rather fun too.

Sometimes I wonder what would it be like,
to be back in the wild again,
but when ma comes home,
and everything's fun,
who cares wherever I am!

Elinor Ross (11)
Presdales School

THE WIND IN THE TREES

The wind it flows
Through glistening rows
Of beautiful lime green trees
They swing and they sway
As the wind goes away
Those beautiful lime green trees
I am up there
With the wind in my hair
Up in those lime green trees
It feels like the sea
Is swirling round me
Up in those lime green trees.

Ruth Woodrow (11)
Presdales School

THE SILENT THIEF

The creeping shadows in the night
The old wooden door creaks slowly open.
There stands the thief in all of his might
With a proud and superior stare.

He crept across the frozen marble
His claws scratching and slipping
Against what seemed like frozen ice
What is this creature that roams the night?

His eyes glint as an enemy approaches,
He tries to hold on to the shadows.
But the candlelight creeps in
and the trembling voice screams . . .
Rat!

Hannah Copley (11)
Presdales School

ONE TO TEN

One wicked wolf wandered into the wilderness
Two tiny twins toddled in Tesco's
Three thoughtless thugs thumped thunderously
Four frisky foals found a fresh field
Five fast fishes flipped funnily
Six silly sailors sailed the seven seas
Seven stupid snakes slithered slyly
Eight awful apes ate appetising apricots
Nine nasty natterers nattered naughtily
Ten tidy tortoises tiptoed thoughtfully.

Amy Himsworth (11)
Presdales School

THE FUTURE . . .

What·will the future be like for me?
In my dreams I can sometimes see . . .

Your friends will be robots with their own mind,
You'll live with aliens as well as mankind.
The Earth would have moved next door to Mars
Wouldn't it be great to touch the stars?

People would be free, independent with their land,
You wouldn't be kicked down but left to stand.
There would be no debt, poverty or wars,
An independent country with its own laws.

We can always dream of our future which is near,
Should this be a thing that many people fear?
It's time to let go and throw away the past,
As the millennium is coming very, very fast!

Rhian Roberts (14)
Presdales School

CATS

Cats are wonderful things
They bend down low and jump up high.
They jump up high to catch a fly or maybe even a butterfly.
They bend down low to catch a feather
But something fluffy would be better.
When they were kittens they would play with mittens.
In their senior years their greatest fears would be wet, soggy tears.

Claire Lawlor (11)
Presdales School

THE COLOUR OF MY SKIN

Standing on the outside, always looking in,
Why am I not the same as them?
I've never been respected for the person I really am,
All because of one small thing, the colour of my skin.

How would you feel being stared at,
Called names, kicked, abused,
Forever alone, never having friends,
All because of one small thing, the colour of my skin.

Every day I'm told and told,
Ignore them and stand up for myself,
How would they know what I go through?
All because of one small thing, the colour of my skin.

Perhaps one day, when I'm grown-up,
I'll move back to the country where I'm from,
There I might lead a trouble-free life
Without worrying about the colour of my skin.

Claire Green (13)
Presdales School

MEOW!

The cat curls up in a furry ball
Waiting to jump and frighten you in the hall.
He purrs when you tickle his head
Then sleeps next to you in your bed.
He jumps at moving objects,
He fights with the cats outside.
But it does not bother me
I love cats eternally.

Elizabeth North (11)
Presdales School

ROSE BLANCHE

Out in the forest
gloomy and dull.
Soldiers may be hiding
in the shadows of the trees.

She follows the van
to a dark camp site.
Where people are standing,
miserable, pale and cold.
Hungry eyes stare at her face.

They are dressed in stripes,
and wearing a David's Star.
These poor Jewish people
I must get them some food.

Rose hurried home and told not a soul
what she had seen that day.
She saved her own food and gave it
to the poor people who were thankful
for they were trapped behind electric wires.

One day when everybody in the town left
Rose went to the camp site.
She was shocked, for no one was there,
she thought that they had been killed.
She placed a flower
on the barbed wire and heard a shot
from a gun.
Her mother never saw her kind-hearted
daughter again.

Victoria Wray (12)
Presdales School

I WONDER!

I wonder why the sea is blue
I wonder why it's deep
I wonder why it's always there
Even when we sleep.

I wonder why the sky is there
I wonder why it's high.
I wonder why it all goes dark
When the sun's gone by.

I wonder why the stars are white,
I wonder why they gleam.
I wonder why they disappear
When the sun begins to beam.

I wonder why the sun is round
I wonder why it's bright.
I wonder why it's far away,
And disappears at night.

Sarah Withers (11)
Presdales School

MUM

Thanks for being so wonderful
For all the things you do
To make my world a better place
For being ever patient and giving me your love
And for loving everyone else
Just by being you.

Amisha Majithia (11)
Presdales School

FROM AN OLD LADY'S HEART

I'm going on holiday in outer space
I'm in a rocket, I love this place.
When I was a child we used to hop on a plane.
We could only fly somewhere on Earth like Spain.
We have nearly reached to the Moon,
I'm hoping to glance at some aliens soon.
I remember my mum, the house she would clean.
Now robots do it, so no more Mr Sheen
I do feel depressed when I think of the old days,
People did more and lived in different ways.
I am old now and have lived a lot of pleasure,
My life in my heart, I will always treasure.

Claire-Louise Hagon (13)
Presdales School

THE COLOURLESS SEA

I sit on the shore
Of the colourless sea
Thinking about the birds and the bees.
The buzzing sound
That runs through the trees.
The tweeting sound that lurks around me
The sound of footsteps that I can hear.
The smell of flowers that wave when I'm near.
The dancing of treetops, that I can see
The love that flows in the colourless sea.

Amanda Feeney (12)
Presdales School

FUTURE PLANET

When 2100 comes
things will be different.
With metal-looking clothes
and a metal-looking kitchen.

Silver-leaved trees
and silver rain falls.
Travelling so high
in the pitch black of nigh.

There will be no cars
spaceships instead.
Visiting lots of planets
wearing cosmic hats.

2100 will be a good year
as you can gather
I wish I was there
and you there with me!

Donna Glazebrook (13)
Presdales School

DISCO

The beat of the drum booms through the huge speakers,
stomping and dancing feet like walking
elephants fill the room, and dance floor.
People shouting and laughing,
Excessive heat is making you want to faint,
the stuffiness makes you want to gasp for air.
The DJ speaks, it goes silent!
Then the booming beat starts banging once again.
And the process is repeated . . .

Stacey Doyle (12)
Presdales School

I WONDER . . .

I wonder how the future will be?
Will there be a lot more to see?
Modern technology here we come
It's now time to have some fun.

I wonder how we will dress?
Will it still be a stress?
We might be dressed, we might be bare,
We may just be in underwear!

I wonder what we will eat?
Will there be such a thing as meat?
Maybe we won't eat at all
And end up small or even tall.

I'm glad that I'll still have my mother,
But please, please don't give me a brother!

Angela Ferraro (13)
Presdales School

THE SWANS

There they swim,
gracefully on the water's skin.
With feathers white as snow,
and feet that paddle fast and slow.
When they want they fly away,
and maybe come back another day,
they have a family on their back.
So there they swim,
gracefully on the water's skin.

Sophie Hanson (11)
Presdales School

A FUTURE PLACE

There is a place
far away
Or maybe it's close
I cannot say.
It's full of changes
so different from now.
Of bright pink elephants
and a lime green cow.

There is a place
it'll be here soon.
It's closer thank you think
but further than the moon.
It's bright and colourful
a place to play.
Full of happiness,
forever and a day.

Claire Martin (14)
Presdales School

THE HOLOCAUST

H appiness is stolen away
O ver six million people killed
L ots of piles of shoes and glasses
O nly a few people survived
C rying children left alone
A ttacked because of their religion
U nwanted by their countries
S eparated from loved ones
T errible things happened to Jews.

Lucy Houghton (13)
Presdales School

THE FUTURE

The future is happy and bright,
And when we get there,
We will see the most beautiful sight,
A sight cared for with tender loving care.

Light, light everywhere,
So beautiful and pretty too.
I can't wait to get there.
Can you?

Everyone is equal in this place,
Christians, Muslims, blacks and whites,
People of every race,
There is no need to scratch and bite.

The future is so near,
Yet also so far.
You won't find it near here,
No matter where you travel, or how far.

No one can wait for it,
Everybody wants it now.
Unfortunately we'll have to wait a bit,
But every passing minute brings it nearer than now.

Kate Edmunds (13)
Presdales School

For The Future

What is a pen for the future?
A computer is our pen
What is poverty for the future?
One meal at Burger King.

What are guns for the future?
A tool that's there for free.
What is an unlocked door for the future?
A card not a simple, old key.

What is a crime for the future?
Not drugs or death or war.
What about people for the future?
The homeless with clothes all torn.

What is murder for the future?
A sadness always to come.
Wanting to be free for the future?
Wanting to go, stupid to some.

What is help, comfort for the future?
What's this? It will sort out.
A hand to hold for the future!
A hand to hold without a doubt.

Jennie Lane (13)
Presdales School

The Song Of The Whale

The song of the whale plays high and low,
But of all who hear, but a few will know,
Of the tale of sadness that's in their history,
For most the whale shall remain a mystery.

It tells of their life and the calves that were born,
Of swimming in moonlight, rising with the dawn,
They jump through the water, leap through the air,
These magnificent creatures that now are so rare.

Lianne Riches (13)
Presdales School

DREAMING

Lying on a sun-kissed beach,
Drinking freshly squeezed orange,
Dolphins jumping on the horizon,
I'm dreaming.

Shopping all day in Paris,
Eating all evening in Prague,
Staying in all different countries,
I'm dreaming.

Dancing with my prince charming,
A flowing satin ball gown,
A glittering carriage awaits me,
I'm dreaming.

I will escape from here one day,
I'll start a whole new life,
I'll be a new person one day,
I won't be dreaming anymore.

Kate Walters (13)
Presdales School

REMEMBERING

Painted faces smile down at you
Sitting cross-legged on the stained carpet
Listening entranced by a fantasy story
Scrambling back to create your own world of witches and fairies
Splodges of colour brighten your shirt.

10am on the playmobile clock
Rush outside to the inviting playground
Red metal mazes and big wooden horses
Run and tumble on the cruel concrete
Tears run down in a stream-like trickle.

Your favourite teacher sits you on her knee
And reaches for some dolly mixtures
The familiar sound of squeaky chalk
As you practise the alphabet
Glance at the friendly hamster, whiskers twitching
As he stares unblinkingly back.

Everyone cheers as the teacher plays her guitar
Singing loud and tunefully to *The Yellow Submarine.*
Endless rounds of your favourite songs
Until it's time to go home and you run
Across to your smiling mum.

Anna Hawker (13)
Presdales School

CANDLELIT BRIDGE

'Can you see that candlelit bridge?'
'I can, I can' says little Midge.
'I can see that candlelit bridge.'

'It's such fun to run in and out of it.
It's like a summer sun, and you're in a hot pit
It's so nice I don't care when I get bit.'

It's such a nice flame of a candle,
It's like a burning handle,
It's like a hot, sweaty sandal.

Midge, Midge, Midge remember Midgey Midge.
Do you remember Midge?
Hey, hey, it's Midge, Midge, Midgey-Midge?

Emma Sampford (11)
Presdales School

WHAT DOES THE FUTURE HOLD?

In the year 2033,
The world will be gone,
But I'll still be me,
We'll all live in space
And drive flying machines
Everywhere silver and not very green.
A single tablet will quench your thirst for a week,
We'll all be telepathic,
We won't have to speak.
Clothes will be grey,
Without any colour.
But that's a long way away,
I'll just concentrate on today.

Katie Buckingham (14)
Presdales School

LONGING FOR LOVE

They rush past
Rosy-cheeked and invigorated
From frantic, last minute Christmas shopping.

She shuffles on
Pale, head down,
Oblivious to
The twinkling High Street decorations,
The joy and eagerness in young faces,
The lusty singing of the carollers,
Lost in her own world of the past
When her husband was alive
When life was good
When she was loved.

A few glance pitying
At the sad, lifeless eyes,
Her dejected air.

Teenage girls nudge and giggle
At her dowdy old-fashioned skirt
Two sizes too big.

Darkness falls, and with it
Rain.

And still she shuffles on.

She stops and gazes through a lit window:
Sees merry Christmas-tree lights,
Warmth,
Happiness,
Affection.

She gazes on
And longs to be loved.

Katherine Woollgar (13)
Presdales School

FAME!

You could be a famous actress,
You could be a pop star,
But unlike some people I know,
Don't let it forget who you are!

Some people cover themselves,
With jewellery and make-up,
I don't see why they bother,
It comes off on a teacup!

I'd like to be famous,
But I just couldn't,
I'd have to change my life around,
So I guess I really wouldn't.

Everyone wants a bit of fame,
I think it's too much to ask,
I'd better think about it for a while,
So for now I think I'll *pass!*

Lisa Gould (11)
Presdales School

MIDDLE

Middle - what a horrible word.
It's not good, it's not bad,
It's not first, it's not last,
It's not old, it's not young,
It's non-committal.

For instance:

The first child is the eldest,
The responsible, achieving one.

The last is the youngest,
The baby of the family.

The middle is the backup plan,
If something goes wrong,
Or the expectations are not met.

Also.

The under-achiever is supported,
Encouraged or told to get on with it
The over-achiever is praised,
Named and rewarded.

But the middle student is ignored.
No reason to show support,
Encourage or call upon.

Middle - what a horrible word.
What can we do?

We can only hope,
That from its secure little home,
One middle speaks up.
Achieves something no one else has ever done.
Stands out.

But then, wouldn't that mean
They were no longer a middle?

Rebecca Andrews (17)
Presdales School

THROUGH THE EYES OF A CHILD

The classroom is bright and cheerful,
Self-portraits on the wall,
Self portraits painted in primary colours,
Still wet and dripping with imagination.

The teacher always smiling,
Guides you when you are wrong,
Talks you through step by step,
Treated as one of her own.

The playroom filled with fantasies,
Awash with toys and books,
Swallows you up when you've been good,
A magical place of happiness.

We learn to read, count and spell,
Each day a new adventure,
The classroom shines with challenges,
Absorbed by every child.

Carly Roberts (13)
Presdales School

SORRY DAD

Dad I'm sorry,
Dad I was wrong,
Dad please listen to what I must say.

Dad I was bad,
I made you angry,
I made you sad,
But only if you would understand why.

Thirteen is a terrible age,
All confused with the thoughts of growing up!
Losing my temper over silly little things,
Now this is where it all starts to begin.

Make-up, music, television, shops,
Buying lots of slinky, colourful tops,
This is all I'm thinking of,
So I hope that you will understand,
The unusual, abstract, wonderland,
And twist your head round to thinking about forgiving and forgetting.

Victoria Mills (13)
Presdales School

PEACE, LOVE AND UNITY

This is what I plan to create
Black and white will congregate
smooth like chocolate
silk like gold.

Peace, love and unity
That's what I really want to see
if you like it, like me
can you see what I see?

Together is where we'll be
in the rave of harmony
What a place it would be
feeling love and ecstasy.

Kelly Finley (13)
Presdales School

I'M THE SAME AS YOU . . .

People don't often talk to me,
the wheelchair is all that they see.
When I was younger, I didn't know why,
but I understood, as time went by.

The only thing different is that I can't walk,
I can do everything else, like hear, see and talk.
I'm not an outsider, I'm the same as you,
give me a chance to prove what I can do.

When I go out, some people just stare,
but others walk by and don't turn a hair.
Everyone's different, that's plain to see,
so why do people keep looking at me?

Despite the chair, I have a mind of my own,
I too can work, and run my own home.
The world is a place, where we all should be equal,
so stop, think and consider other people.

Jenna Singleton (13)
Presdales School

HOLIDAYS OF THE FUTURE

In the future the holidays will be to,
A place the scientists call the moon.
We'll pack our bags for outer space,
And leave this planet without a trace,

Holidays to the Bahamas are so last season,
And they've disappeared without a reason.
The sea, the sun is not now around,
Instead there's space without the ground.

The future holidays are looking bright,
But can't get there without a flight.
The future holidays are looking to be,
Such fun and so exciting I can't wait to see.

Emma Bines (13)
Presdales School

THINKING

You sit there staring
Into space
I wonder what you're thinking about
Your facial expressions
Make me frown
The look in your sparkling eyes
Makes me smile
You're thinking hard
But what about?
The expression on your face
The sparkle in your eyes
I can't put together
What you're thinking about.

Nicola Turner (13)
Presdales School

CLASS ONE

I can still remember that reassuring scent of the classroom,
That security and warmth,
that one room could bring.

The vivid displays that carpeted the walls,
The mountain of toys that cluttered a corner.

The elephant-grey desks with
flimsy child-sized chairs,
And our own individual name cards,
that made us feel special.

The inviting and enchanting book corner,
Where you could drift away into your own
magical fantasy.

Our kind and affectionate teacher,
Mrs Ellis,
who loved us all as individuals and
welcomed us with open arms -

To our new life we were to lead,
in a classroom,
we could call our own.

Victoria Marshall (13)
Presdales School

Do You Remember?

Do you remember
That first day when your world became the classroom?
You were scared at first,
But then remembered you were a big girl now.

The cartons of milk
Lined up in rows like soldiers,
Standing to attention
Until we gulped them down.

Out in the playground
Shrieks and squeals could be heard
From the game of kiss chase on the field
And you cried because the little fat boy actually kissed you!

Annie Apple, Bouncing Ben,
Learning how to count to ten.
The vibrant patterns on the walls,
A haven of colour surrounded you.

'Rachel, Rachel, are you listening?
Tell me what you thought of your infant schooldays,'
I turned and smiled.
Do you remember? I remember . . .

Rachel Perlman (13)
Presdales School

A CLASSROOM SCENE

Brightly coloured paper on the walls
Books stacked up in alphabetical order
sitting on the carpet for story time,
sugar paper shapes and my work on the wall
Things I can just remember.

The smell of freshly sharpened pencils
Milk piled up by the window
cushions fluffed and ready for story time
Dusty chalk smells and board rubbers
Things I yearn to remember.

PE times
Lunchtimes and
playtimes, my favourite
Things I used to look forward to.

Colouring in pictures the teacher has drawn
Trying desperately hard not to go over the line
The naughty boy jogs you
It's okay, don't cry
Things I wish I still had.

Jessica Reed (13)
Presdales School

FIRST IMPRESSIONS

The vibrant exotic colours of my new world merge,
As my eyes fill with fearful, anxious tears.
I fight them back, a battle hard to win.
'I am a big girl now,' I chant, as I will myself to go on.

The smell of bleach and cleanliness hurls itself at me.
Pristine, white walls, scattered with images.
My eyes dart fretfully, from one person to another,
Desperate for a familiar face.

She stands tall in one corner,
Nervous tension tightens the taut air.
A false smile stands imprinted on her lips,
Frosty eyes seem to glare like icebergs catching the morning light.

A low, strong voice escapes from her stiff lips,
I quiver as I feel my throat dry like a desert in the sun.
The battle of maturity commences,
Slowly, sadly the salty tears begin to fall.

She moves swiftly towards me.
I catch a smile cross her lips,
She whispers a reassuring word in my ear,
Warily, I let down my guard.

Although forbidding at first,
I know I will grow to love.
A motherly air emanates from her,
That every young child can sense.

I have finally now moved on,
My world is now but a classroom.
All security and trust lies here,
As the reality of *big girl* dawns.

Alex Fitzpatrick (13)
Presdales School

LOCKED IN

There is nothing strange about my appearance,
To make me stand out in a crowd,
My hair and clothes are standard,
But my eyes and head stay bowed.

I have always felt an outsider,
I knew I didn't belong,
A reclusive, solitary childhood,
A foreigner getting everything wrong.

My perplexed and baffled parents,
Were desperate to understand why.
Endless appointments and consultations,
Just bewildered and mystified.

My primary encounters with schooling,
Illustrated my cloistered existence,
A padlocked book without a key,
Wary mothers and children keep their distance.

I stared as those around me,
Effortlessly managed to comply,
I was a puzzle with pieces missing,
Their game rules simply wouldn't apply.

Eventually the hidden pieces were found,
The key to the lock began to turn,
A diagnosis of autism was given,
So the rules of life I must learn.

Olivia Harris (13)
Presdales School

DIFFERENT

He lurks in the shadows,
scared to show his face,
everybody laughs at him,
loathes him for his race.

He strolls up and down the streets,
scared and all alone,
such a sense of isolation,
he longs to be at home.

Back there things were different,
people took him as he came,
they shared his thoughts and dreams
and treated him the same.

Then he had to move,
to start a brand-new life,
but it wasn't quite as he had thought,
it led to pain and strife.

Nobody will talk to him,
frightened of what he'll do,
but why do they have to worry?
He's just like me and you.

Sarah Wilkinson (13)
Presdales School

THE OLD MAN AT THE COVE

The old man sitting in that chair,
thinking of his past,
in an orphanage most of his life,
now he's free at last,
met his wife at a ballroom dance,
now she's died and gone,
all his family have left him,
and he's been alone so long,
his small pale complexion,
is all wrinkled up,
his bloodshot eyes
look at you sharply,
but then they turn so soft,
his hair flickers in the wind,
just like feathers of grey,
in his tiny grass hut,
he watches the tide flow away,
the fruits in his garden,
are full of pride and joy,
most of the time he's out there,
treating them like his boys,
this poor old man is lonely,
he wants some company,
he's been alone most of his life,
overlooking the sea.

Abigail Laura Hart (11)
Presdales School

MUMMY'S LITTLE ANGEL

Mummy went into hospital yesterday,
Daddy wouldn't tell me why, at first.
I thought she might be ill.
But then Grandma told me,
'Your mummy's going to have a little angel.
A baby girl, won't that be nice?'
No I'm Mummy's little angel
Or I used to be.
They wouldn't like it if they knew,
But they wouldn't let me in the room.
Mummy said I wouldn't like it,
I wouldn't. She doesn't want me anymore.
So I'm sitting here on my own.
I don't like waiting rooms.
I don't like the Beano or Woman's Own,
But I hate the baby.
So I'm banging my feet on the floor and staring,
Staring out of the window, watching the rain.
A nurse is here in a long white coat,
I've got to go and see the baby,
I don't want to but I am.
We're at the door. We're going in.
Mummy's smiling, Daddy's smiling, Baby's smiling,
And I'm smiling.
I think I might like having a sister.
Just maybe.
But for now I'm Mummy's little angel anyway.

Catherine Cruse (12)
Presdales School

THE COMING OF THE COLD

T ales told from leaf to leaf as they
H ang desperately from a bough like a clinging monkey, longing that
E very breath will not be their last.

C hlorophyll has long since rotted and just a bony skeleton remains
O n a chilly winter's afternoon.
M artial artist Jack Frost under
I nstruction from Hanker Chief Winter;
N othing can stop him from
G lazing the whole earth with his

O dious sheet of paralysing ice.
F rom soft to stiff the grass blades turn overnight.

T he farmer's seed furrows are filled with
H oary,
E ndless ice;

C lear, thick and unbreakable
O nlookers watch hunched sparrows as they peck desperately,
L onging that the ice will break so they may have a
D rink.

Matthew Bee (14)
Richard Hale School